RESPONSES
Wordlife
RICHARD KNOTT
D0537927
WITHDRAWN
THE RIDGE COLLEGE LIBRARY
HIBBERT LANE, MARPLE
STOCKPORT SK6 7PA
WITHDRAWN
Ridge Danyers College : Marple Campus
* M0006512 *

Thomas Nelson and Sons Ltd
Nelson House Mayfield Road
Walton-on-Thames Surrey
KT12 5PL UK

51 York Place
Edinburgh
EH1 3JD UK

Thomas Nelson (Hong Kong) Ltd
Toppan Building 10/F
22A Westlands Road
Quarry Bay Hong Kong

Distributed in Australia by

Thomas Nelson Australia
480 La Trobe Street
Melbourne Victoria 3000
and in Sydney, Brisbane, Adelaide and Perth

First published by Thomas Nelson and Sons Ltd 1988

ISBN 0-17-432177–5
NPN 9 8 7 6 5 4 3 2 1

Printed and bound in Hong Kong

The author wishes to thank the following for their ideas and inspiration: Trevor Dickinson HMI; John Taylor HMI; Steve Cooper; Les Albiston; Patrick and Angel Scott.

RESPONSES

Series editors: Angel and Patrick Scott

Community Writing by Don Shiach
Frankie Mae and other stories by Ann Mann and Hilary Rich
Wordlife by Richard Knott

Editors' note

GCSE reflects the most interesting and successful initiatives in English teaching that have taken place over the last 15 to 20 years. As a consequence it is no longer possible to ignore classroom talk, or to pretend that 'response' doesn't play an important part in reading, and 'variety' in writing. No longer can the English curriculum be sliced up into lessons on 'comprehension' or 'essay writing' or 'spelling'; the constituent parts of the subject are 'clearly inter-related and interdependent' (National Criteria for GCSE) and one activity has to grow naturally out of another.

The series builds on these principles. It aims to make available for pupils some of the best contemporary sources ranging from familiar literary genres, like poetry or the short story, to less conventional forms, like community writing. The 'follow-on' work that is included at the back of each book suggests ways in which the material might be used to provoke discussion, develop ideas for folios of work and introduce new ways of reading texts. That is why the series as a whole is called '*Responses*'.

Angel and Patrick Scott

CONTENTS

■ INTRODUCTION ■

Poetry teaching should be low profile, invitational, inclusive in its material and approaches. We should mediate less between the texts and the children; we should aim to give poems back to their readers.

(*Mike Benton*)

At the moment, if you're seen reading poetry in a train, the carriage empties instantly.

(*Andrew Motion, quoted by Wendy Cope in* Making Cocoa for Kingsley Amis)

Since I was eight I learnt everything I could about poetry and I was determined to make a success out of my life. I have written one poetry book and it has nineteen poems but I am making it bigger.

(*Eleven year old pupil, Slough, Berkshire*)

The eleven year old quoted above is living proof that poetry can hold a powerful grip on children. Regrettably, if Andrew Motion is right in seeing adult readers of poetry as social outcasts, it could well be the result of bitter memories of poetry teaching at school. One fourth year pupil undergoing 'O' level a few years ago summed up the damage: 'If I was given the choice of never to do poetry again, I would not do it. In my life, reading poetry – never have I enjoyed it. I would arrange separate classes for children who wanted to do it'.

It need not be like that of course: the opening quotation should be carved on every English teacher's desk! It is the reason why there are no specific exercises tied to individual poems in this anthology. The teacher's role in sharing and exploring poetry with a class is to provide an opening into the poetry's language and mood, to allow a response to grow, to provide interest; it is not to reduce the verse to a treadmill of questions on a dog-eared worksheet. Poetry should not be something that you 'do', but an experience you share and which, in Heaney's telling phrase, causes words to rumble powerfully through the 'echo chamber of the head'.

It was in order to stop themselves from making poetry an imposition that a group of teachers devised the following guidelines for their own practice.

Teaching Poetry: things to remember

- The range and variety of poetry is important.
- The poetry shared with children should be relevant to their experience.
- It should be enjoyed.
- Children should often hear poems read aloud.
- Involving pupils in the poem matters.
- The children should understand that it is response to poetry that matters most.
- Pupils should have, at times, the freedom to choose what poems they read.
- It is not always appropriate for the pupils' response to be written.
- Teachers should be seen to be readers of poetry.
- Poetry needs to be given status in the classroom not introduced apologetically.

If the ten principles in this list had to be condensed into a single sentence, the first priority would have to be the inclusion of some reference to 'personal response'. This is the key to the successful sharing of poetry with pupils in the classroom. The title of Peter Benton's book *Pupil, Teacher, Poem* provides a valuable model: the individual is placed first. We must, therefore, recognise (and plan for) the need for the poem to 'speak' to pupils. Teachers, however, come a very close second in importance. The approach they choose to adopt, their methodology and their interventions, are obviously critical. Pupils must feel that classroom activities open up the poetry to them, and do not kill it off. Finally, there is the poem itself. If the teacher's interventions are 'low key and invitational', then the poem retains its voice.

- What happens when we read poems?
- Are there qualities which all poems share?
- How can we encourage personal response?
- How can we translate what we know about reading poems into ways of teaching them?

(*Benton and Fox,* Teaching Literature 9–14)

One way of making a start on those four questions posed by Mike Benton and Geoff Fox, is to take a look at what the pupils say. In *Examining Poetry – the Need for Change*, John Dixon and Leslie Stratta provide advice based on what some pupils think will help them come to terms with poetry. This is the list they have compiled.

- Don't produce another comprehension exercise.
- Offer a handrail (in case help is needed).
- Be simple and direct (preventing confusion).
- Arouse interest in the poem.
- Show interest in 'me' and 'my' reactions.
- Encourage me to look further into the poem.
- Prompt me to think . . . delve . . . tease out relevancies and hidden meanings.
- Allow me to ignore prompts and add my own views.

Perhaps the most striking thing about this list is that all the advice lays great stress on the skill of the teacher. The pupil is unlikely to value poetry unless the teacher feels that way about it too. Vernon Scannell once wrote that 'Poetry is a Tiger! The teacher must love poetry but must not be a poetry lover, must never try to turn the thing into a sacred cow . . . '. Teachers, it would seem, must be positive about poetry without allowing their own enthusiasms to dominate the classroom. They must wait for a response to emerge, without forcing the pace. They must trust to the poem and the pupil whilst knowing that their own actions will determine the success of the encounter. It's a difficult path to tread.

One way of negotiating all the obstacles and pitfalls is to 'withdraw and let the pupils talk'. All of the poems in this anthology are appropriate for small group discussion. Such talk can be 'structured', in the sense that the direction of the talk is pre-determined by questions, or it can be entirely free – where there is no set agenda and the pupils decide for themselves what they talk about. One group of fourth years working on '*About Friends*' (p. 2) were asked to read the poem and then talk about what they found interesting or difficult to understand. They were working in a self-selected friendship group; the teacher was not with them.

Mark:	I know a bit I don't understand.
David:	What?
Mark:	Last line on the second paragraph . . . third paragraph . . . 'we should not be,. and were somehow ashamed.'
David:	No . . . 'cos that feels like they was little doing this by the river banks.
Darren:	Yes – now they've got to do it all again . . . things have changed.
David:	And they got caught sort of thing . . .
Mark:	Ashamed of not knowing . . .
Darren:	Yeah . . . of not knowing what they were going to say.
Paul:	They feel ashamed of finishing their sentences because they are not like they were twenty years ago.
David:	Yeah, 'cos they think about the laugh and a joke . . .
Mark:	Because they didn't understand each other.

This extract is part of a longer discussion in which the pupils cover a lot of ground, far more than in a conventional 'question and answer' setting. In a poem about friendship and time gone past, it is fascinating to hear four friends discussing lines like: 'the good thing about friends/ is not having to finish sentences . . .' and themselves finding no need to finish sentences . . .

Two additional examples of this kind of free ranging discussion are provided in the HMI booklet, *Teaching Poetry in the Secondary School*, where groups of pupils are asked to 'unpack the poem's meaning' (referring to Kit Wright's, 'January Birth') and to discuss 'The Warm and the Cold' by Ted Hughes. HMI stress that discussion of this kind 'shifts the emphasis from teaching poetry to learning how to read and experience poetry'.

When poetry works as successfully as this, it is possible, with confidence, to locate it at the centre of work in English. For poetry to remain deeply embedded in the mainstream of work in English, however, departments need to have an explicit and agreed policy on poetry and its management in the classroom throughout the school. If they do not, it may become 'the excess baggage that gets ditched when the going gets tough'. Such a policy would involve the following initiatives:

- the writing and reading of poetry by teachers;
- redrafting as an accepted feature of pupils' writing;
- poems being 'published';
- collections of poems made available and visible (including 'solo' collections);

- departmental meetings in which there are structured opportunities for the sharing of poetry;
- classroom environments which enable purposeful, but tentative, sharing of poetry;
- a recognition that in literature above all 'the teacher must get out of the way'.

A departmental policy ought also to tackle questions like these.

- How does the department raise the status of poetry?
- What 'technical language' do the pupils need in order to talk and write about poetry?
- How is that 'metalanguage' introduced?
- What are the resource implications of your policy for poetry?
- 'Withdraw and let the pupils talk'. How and when?
- What is the right balance of modern poetry with 'the classics'?

Amidst all this necessary planning, it should not be forgotten that poetry is a distinct literary genre that should be taught as such, and not reduced to 'fitting the theme'. In Peter Abbs' words,

> . . . Structuralism provides us with the principles of genre. Informed by this principle, the teaching of literature becomes, in part, a living and formal initiation into the various genres which comprise it . . . myth, poetry, short story, the novel, drama, autobiography, biography, documentary, the essay etc . . .

The *form* of poetry – that which makes it different – should never be far from the teacher's mind in sharing poetry with the pupils. At the same time, pupils need opportunities to explore poems for themselves providing their own agenda. It is hoped that the poems in *Wordlife* and the suggestions that are made about how they can be studied will help you to 'give poems back to their readers'.

Richard Knott, 1988

■ Tich Miller ■

Tich Miller wore glasses
with elastoplast-pink frames
and one foot three sizes larger than the other.

When they picked teams for outdoor games
she and I were always the last two
left standing by the wire-mesh fence.

We avoided one another's eyes,
stooping, perhaps, to re-tie a shoelace,
or affecting interest in the flight

of some fortunate bird, and pretended
not to hear the urgent conference:
'Have Tubby!' 'No, no, have Tich!'

Usually they chose me, the lesser dud,
and she lolloped, unselected,
to the back of the other team.

At eleven we went to different schools.
In time I learned to get my own back,
sneering at hockey-players who couldn't spell.

Tich died when she was twelve.

Wendy Cope

■ About Friends ■

The good thing about friends
Is not having to finish sentences.

I sat a whole summer afternoon with my friend once
on a river bank, bashing heels on the baked mud
and watching the small chunks slide into the water
and listening to them – plop plop plop.
He said 'I like the twigs when they . . . you know . . .
like that.' I said 'There's that branch. . . .'
We both said 'Mmmm.' The river flowed and flowed
and there were lots of butterflies, that afternoon.

I first thought there was a sad thing about friends
when we met twenty years later.
We both talked hundreds of sentences,
taking care to finish all we said,
and explain it all very carefully,
as if we'd been discovered in places
we should not be, and were somehow ashamed.

I understood then what the river meant by flowing.

Brian Jones

Miss Creedle Teaches Creative Writing

'This morning,' cries Miss Creedle,
'We're all going to use our imaginations,
We're going to close our eyes 3W and imagine.
Are we ready to imagine Darren?
I'm going to count to three.
At one, we wipe our brains completely clean;
At two, we close our eyes;
And at three, we imagine.
Are we all imagining? Good.
Here is a piece of music by Beethoven to help us.
Beethoven's dates were 1770 to 1827.
(See the Age of Revolutions in your History books.)
Although Beethoven was deaf and a German
He wrote many wonderful symphonies,
But this was a long time before anyone of us was born.
Are you imagining a time before you were born?
What does it look like? Is it dark?
(Embryo is a good word you might use.)
Does the music carry you away like a river?
What is the name of the river? Can you smell it?
Foetid is an exciting adjective.
As you float down the river
Perhaps you land on an alien planet.
Tell me what sounds you hear.
If there are indescribable monsters
Tell me what they are but not now.
(Your book entitled Tackle Pre-History This Way
Will be of assistance here.)
Perhaps you are cast adrift in a broken barrel.
In stormy shark-infested waters
(Remember the work we did on piranhas for RE?)
Try to see yourself. Can you do that?
See yourself at the bottom of a pothole in the Andes
With both legs broken
And your life ebbing away inexorably.
What does the limestone feel like?
See the colours?

Have you done that? Good.
And now you may open your eyes.
Your imagining time is over,
Now it is writing time.
Are we ready to write? Good.
Then write away.
Wayne, you're getting some exciting ideas down.
Tracy, that's lovely.
Darren, you haven't written anything.
Couldn't you put the date?
You can't think of anything to write.
Well, what did you see when you closed your eyes?
But you must have seen something beside the black.
Yes, apart from the little squiggles.
Just the black. I see.
Well, try to think
Of as many words for black as you can.'

Miss Creedle whirls about the class
Like a benign typhoon
Spinning from one quailing homestead to another.
I dream of peaceful ancient days
In Mr Swindell's class
When the hours passed like a dream
Filled with order and measuring and tests.
Excitement is not one of the things I come to school for.
I force my eyes shut
Kicking ineffectually at the starter;
But all I see
Is a boy of twelve
Sitting at a desk one dark November day
Writing this poem.
And Darren is happy to discover
There is only one word for black
And that will have to suffice
Until the bell rings for all of us.

Gareth Owen

■ St. John's School ■

When I went back the school was rather small
but not unexpectedly or oddly so.
I peered in at the windows of the hall
where we sang O God Our Help thirty years ago
for D-Day, the Normandy landings. It was all
as I'd pictured it. Outside, they'd cut the row

of dusty laurels, laid a lawn instead,
and the prefab classroom at the end was new;
but there were the lavatories, there was the shed
where we sat on rainy days with nothing to do,
giggling; and the beech-trees overhead
whose fallen husks we used to riffle through

for triangular nuts. Yes, all as it should be –
no false images to negotiate,
no shocks. I wandered off contentedly
across the playground, out through the north gate,
down the still knee-straining slope, to see
what sprang up suddenly across the street:

the church, that had hardly existed in my past,
that had lurked behind a tree or two, unknown –
and uncensorious of me as I chased
squirrels over the graves – the church had grown:
high on its huge mound it soared, vast;
and God glared out from behind a tombstone.

Fleur Adcock

■ The Face of Hunger ■

I counted the ribs on his concertina chest
Bones protruding as if chiselled
By a sculptor's hand of famine.

He looked with glazed pupils
Seeing only a bun on some sky-high shelf.

The skin was pale and taut
Like a glove on a doctor's hand.

His tongue darted in and out
Like a chameleon's
Snatching a confetti of flies.

O! child,
Your stomach is a den of lions
Roaring day and night.

Oswald Mbuyiseni Mtshali

Dreaming Black Boy

I wish my teacher's eyes wouldn't
go past me today. Wish he'd know
it's okay to hug me when I kick
a goal. Wish I myself wouldn't
hold back when an answer comes.
I'm no woodchopper now
like all ancestors.

I wish I could be educated
to the best of tune up, and earn
good money and not sink to lick
boots. I wish I could go on every
crisscross way of the globe
and no persons or powers or
hotel keepers would make it a waste.

I wish life wouldn't spend me out
opposing. Wish same way creation
would have me stand it would have
me stretch, and hold high, my voice
Paul Robeson's, my inside eye
a sun. Nobody wants to say
hello to nasty answers.

I wish torch tossers of night
would burn lights for decent times.
Wish plotters in pyjamas would pray
for themselves. Wish people wouldn't
talk as if I dropped from Mars.

I wish only boys were scared
behind bravados, for I could suffer.
I could suffer a big big lot.
I wish nobody would want to earn
the terrible burden I can suffer.

James Berry

■ When you're a GROWN-UP . . . ■

When you're a GROWN-UP
a SERIOUS and SENSIBLE PERSON
When you've stopped being SILLY
you can go out and have babies
and go into a SERIOUS and SENSIBLE shop
and ask for:
Tuftytails, Paddipads, Bikkipegs, Cosytoes
and
Tommy Tippee Teethers.
Sno-bunnies, Visivents, Safeshines
Comfybaths, Dikkibibs
and
Babywipes.
Rumba rattles and Trigger Jiggers
A Whirlee Three, a Finger Flip
or a Quacky Duck.
And if you're very SENSIBLE
you can choose
Easifitz, Babybuggies and a Safesitterstand.
Or is it a
Saferstandsit?
No it's a Sitstandsafe. I can never remember.
I'm sorry but Babytalk is a very difficult language.
It's for adults only.
Like 'X' films
Much too horrible for children.

Michael Rosen

■ For Adam, Nearly Twelve ■

Each spring
reminds of other springs.
This, your last April
as a child,
I remember visiting friends
in your first month.
You, bleating in the house,
lamb cry from the fields,
I rushed indoors and out
not knowing which
my full breasts spurting milk.
I am photographed
through hawthorn flowers
unfocussed, blurred
my blossom,
my face not yet my own.

Driving home
a lorry tailed too closely down a hill.
From my rear mirror
it seemed huge cab
and tyres one inch away
from you, asleep.
I drew in.
Trembling at the wheel
I wept and swore
at all machines and men
that threatened you

as I still do.

Frances Horovitz

■ Christmas Thankyou's ■

Dear Auntie
Oh, what a nice jumper
I've always adored powder blue
and fancy you thinking of
orange and pink
for the stripes
how clever of you!

Dear Uncle
The soap is
terrific
So
useful
and such a kind thought and
how did you guess that
I'd just used the last of
the soap that last Christmas brought

Dear Gran
Many thanks for the hankies
Now I really can't wait for the flu
and the daisies embroidered
in red round the 'M'
for Michael
how
thoughtful of you!

Dear Cousin
What socks!
and the same sort you wear
so you must be
the last word in style
and I'm certain you're right that the
luminous green
will make me stand out a mile

Dear Sister
I quite understand your concern
it's a risk sending jam in the post
But I think I've pulled out
all the big bits
of glass
so it won't taste too sharp
spread on toast

Dear Grandad
Don't fret
I'm delighted
So *don't* think your gift will
offend
I'm not at all hurt
that you gave up this year
and just sent me
a fiver
to spend

Mick Gowar

▪ If I had been called Sabrina or Ann, she said ▪

I'm the only poet with the name.
Can you imagine a prima ballerina named
Marge? Marge Curie, Nobel Prize winner.
Empress Marge. My lady Marge? Rhymes with
large/charge/barge. Workingclass?
Definitely. Any attempt to doll it up
(Mar-gee? Mar-gette? Margelina?
Margarine?) makes it worse. Name
like an oilcan, like a bedroom
slipper, like a box of baking soda,
useful, plain; impossible for foreigners,
from French to Japanese, to pronounce.
My own grandmother called me what
could only be rendered in English
as Mousie. O my parents, what
you did unto me, forever. Even
my tombstone will look like a cartoon.

Marge Piercy

■ Nightride ■

The road unwinding under our wheels
New in the headlamps like a roll of foil.
The rain is a recorder writing tunes
In telegraph wires, kerbs and cats' eyes,
Reflections and the lights of little towns.

He turns his head to look at me.
'Why are you quiet?' Shiny road rhythm,
Rain rhythm, beat of the windscreen wipers,
I push my knee against his in the warmth
And the car thrusts the dark and rain away.

The child sleeps, and I reflect, as I breathe
His brown hair, and watch the apple they gave him
Held in his hot hands, that a tree must ache
With the sweet weight of the round rosy fruit,
As I with Dylan's head, nodding on its stalk.

Gillian Clarke

■ Head of English ■

Today we have a poet in the class.
A real live poet with a published book.
Notice the inkstained fingers girls. Perhaps
we're going to witness verse hot from the press.
Who knows. Please show your appreciation
by clapping. Not too loud. Now

sit up straight and listen. Remember
the lesson on assonance, for not all poems,
sadly, rhyme these days. Still. Never mind.
Whispering's, as always, out of bounds –
but do feel free to raise some questions.
After all, we're paying forty pounds.

Those of you with English Second Language
see me after break. We're fortunate
to have this person in our midst.
Season of mists and so on and so forth.
I've written quite a bit of poetry myself,
am doing Kipling with the Lower Fourth.

Right. That's enough from me. On with the Muse.
Open a window at the back. We don't
want winds of change about the place.
Take notes, but don't write reams. Just an essay
on the poet's themes. Fine. Off we go.
Convince us that there's something we don't know.

Well. Really. Run along now girls. I'm sure
that gave an insight to an outside view.
Applause will do. Thank you
very much for coming here today. Lunch
in the hall? Do hang about. Unfortunately
I have to dash. Tracey will show you out.

Carol Anne Duffy

Remembering St. Mary's Churchyard

It took the two of us an hour or more to climb
the grass side of the hill
we stopped and started looped and
ran great circles in what adults thought
a ten minute walk at most

Between the fencing fringe of oaks
a sweep of grass for rolling in or flopping over dead
and up again at 'Ten' to fight
a path through Viking bracken
crisp as shredded wheat

Lords of the grassy slopes
all day all week all month we had
as far as we could see was ours
the sun would climb above the station
all day long through perfect blue

We climbed the churchyard gate and walked
into a garden in which time stood still
unrecognisable to us no lawns no concrete paths
no flowers we knew no stunted coloured clusters
but mysterious severe like stick-faced spinsters
dowdy speckled bell-shaped heads
and brittle feathered leaves
plants forgotten for a hundred years
We cut them down
and headed for the bench beneath the western wall
to eat our lunch

But never did
for she sat there
crying
with her hands unmoving in her lap
holding a pad of blank white paper
and a pencil

She never looked at us
She never moved
She never even
brought her hands up to her face
to hide her tears
She didn't care
what we might think of her
the mad girl crying on the bench
Not old not old like
Crazy Jack who screamed at cars
in St Anne's Road
but old enough to us
(Less than twenty)
in a summer frock
too tight
stretched taut across
a baby growing
big inside her

We knew that bulk
and what it meant
so what was there to cry about?
Why?
with her sketch pad
open untouched on her lap
Why should she cry
no shame no pride
not trying to stop
or even dry her tears

It didn't seem important
but we walked away as quietly as we could
and in the afternoon
forgot her

Mick Gowar

Poem to My Daughter

'I think I'm going to have it,'
I said, joking between pains.
The midwife rolled competent
sleeves over corpulent milky arms.
'Dear, you never have it,
we deliver it.'
A judgement years proved true.
Certainly I've never had you

as you still have me, Caroline.
Why does a mother need a daughter?
Heart's needle – hostage to fortune –
freedom's end. Yet nothing's more perfect
than that bleating, razor-shaped cry
that delivers a mother to her baby.
The bloodcord snaps that held
their sphere together. The child,
tiny and alone, creates the mother.

A woman's life is her own
until it is taken away
by a first particular cry.
Then she is not alone
but a part of the premises
of everything there is.
A branch, a tide . . . a war.
When we belong to the world
we become what we are.

Anne Stevenson

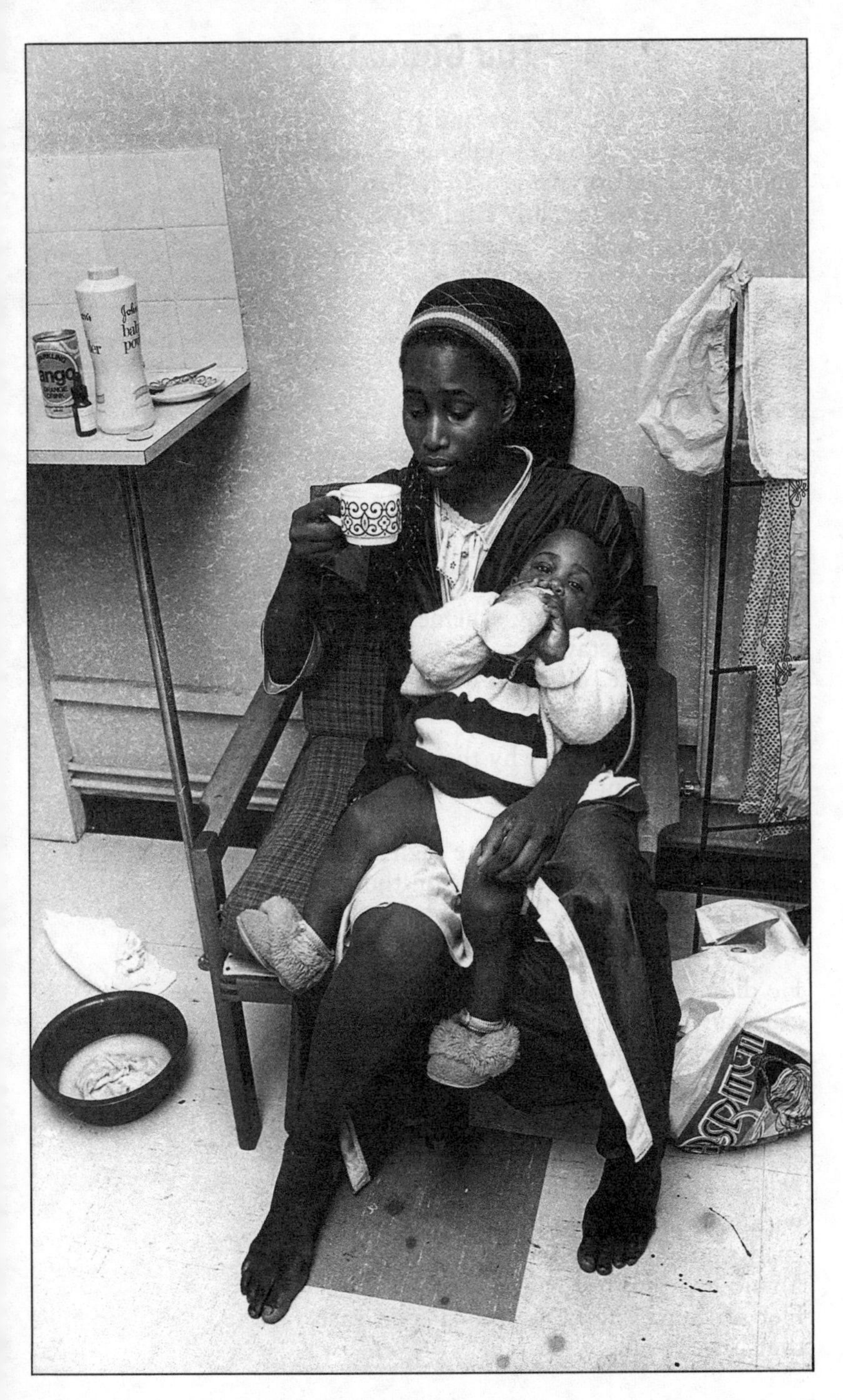

■ The Choosing ■

We were first equal Mary and I
with the same coloured ribbons in mouse-coloured hair,
and with equal shyness
we curtseyed to the lady councillor
for copies of Collins' Children's Classics.
First equal, equally proud.

Best friends too Mary and I
a common bond in being cleverest (equal)
in our small school's small class.
I remember
the competition for top desk
or to read aloud the lesson
at school service.
And my terrible fear
of her superiority at sums.

I remember the housing scheme
where we both stayed.
The same house, different homes,
where the choices were made.

I don't know exactly why they moved, but anyway they went.
Something about a three-apartment
and a cheaper rent.
But from the top deck of the high-school bus
I'd glimpse among the others on the corner
Mary's father, mufflered, contrasting strangely
with the elegant greyhounds by his side.

He didn't believe in high-school education,
especially for girls,
or in forking out for uniforms.

Ten years later on a Saturday –
I am coming home from the library –
sitting near me on the bus,
Mary
with a husband who is tall,
curly haired, has eyes
for no one else but Mary.
Her arms are round the full-shaped vase
that is her body.

Oh, you can see where the attraction lies
in Mary's life –
not that I envy her, really.

And I am coming from the library
with my arms full of books.
I think of the prizes that were ours for the taking
and wonder when the choices got made
we don't remember making.

Liz Lochhead

He Always . . .

He always
He always wanted to explain things, but no one cared,
So he drew.
Sometimes he would just draw and it wasn't anything.
He wanted to carve it in stone or write it in the sky.
He would lie out on the grass and look upon the sky, it would be only the sky and the things inside him that needed saying
And it was after that he drew the picture,
It was a beautiful picture. He kept it under his pillow and
Would let no one see it.
And he would look at it every night and think about it
And when it was dark and his eyes were closed he could see it still.
And it was all of him and he loved it.

When he started school he brought it with him,
Not to show anyone, but just to have with him like a friend.
It was funny about school
He sat in a square brown desk like all the other square desks
and he thought it would be red.
And his room was a square brown room, like all those other rooms.
And it was tight and close. And stiff.
He hated to hold the pencil of chalk, with his arms stiff
and his feet flat on the floor, stiff with the teacher
Watching and watching.
The teacher came and spoke to him.
She told him to wear a tie like all the other boys.
He said he didn't like them and she said it didn't matter.
After that he drew. And he drew all yellow and
it was the way he felt about morning,
And it was beautiful.
The teacher came and smiled at him. 'What's this?' she said.
'Why don't you draw something like Ken's drawing? Isn't it beautiful?'
After that his mother bought him a tie and he always drew airplanes and rocket ships
like everyone else.
And he threw the old pictures away.

And when he lay out alone looking at the sky, it was big and blue, and all
of everything that he wasn't anymore.
He was square and brown inside and his hands were stiff.
And he was like everyone else. All the things inside him that needed saying didn't need it anymore.
It had stopped pushing. It was crushed.
Stiff
Like everything else.

Anon.

The Instant

'We'll go out before breakfast, and get
some mushrooms,' says my mother.

Early, early: the sun
risen, but hidden in mist
the square house left behind
sleeping, filled with sleepers;

up the dewy hill, quietly, with baskets.

Mushrooms firm, cold;
    tussocks of dark grass, gleam of webs,
turf soft and cropped. Quiet and early. And no valley,

no hills: clouds about our knees, tendrils
of cloud in our hair. Wet scrags
of wool caught in barbed wire, gorse
looming, without scent.
                    Then ah! suddenly
the lifting of it, the mist rolls
    quickly away, and far, far –

'Look!' she grips me, 'It is
        Eryri!
            It's Snowdon, fifty
    miles away!' – the voice
a wave rising to Eryri,
falling.
    Snowdon, home
of eagles, resting place of
Merlin, core of Wales.

            Light
graces the mountainhead
for a lifetime's look, before the mist
    draws in again.

Denise Levertov

■ The Skip ■

I took my life and threw it on the skip,
Reckoning the next-door neighbours wouldn't mind
If my life hitched a lift to the council tip
With their dry rot and rubble. What you find

With skips is – the whole community joins in.
Old mattresses appear, doors kind of drift
Along with all that won't fit in the bin
And what the bin-men can't be fished to shift.

I threw away my life, and there it lay
And grew quite sodden. 'What a dreadful shame,'
Clucked some old bag and sucked her teeth: 'The way
The young these days . . . no values . . . me, I blame . . .'

But I blamed no one. Quality control
Had loused it up, and that was that. 'Nough said.
I couldn't stick at home. I took a stroll
And passed the skip, and left my life for dead.

Without my life, the beer was just as foul,
The landlord still as filthy as his wife,
The chicken in the basket was an owl,
And no one said: 'Ee, Jim-lad, whur's thee life?'

Well, I got back that night the worse for wear,
But still just capable of single vision;
Looked in the skip; my life – it wasn't there!
Some bugger'd nicked it – *without* my permission.

Okay, so I got angry and began
To shout, and woke the street. Okay. *Okay*!
And I was sick all down the neighbour's van.
And I disgraced myself on the par-*kay*.

And then . . . you know if you've had a few
You'll wake at dawn, all healthy, like sea breezes,
Raring to go, and thinking: 'Clever you!
You've got away with it.' And then, oh Jesus,

It hits you. Well, that morning, just at six
I woke, got up and looked down at the skip.
There lay my life, still sodden, on the bricks;
There lay my poor old life, arse over tip.

Or was it mine? Still dressed, I went downstairs
And took a long cool look. The truth was dawning.
Someone had just exchanged my life for theirs.
Poor fool, I thought – I should have left a warning.

Some bastard saw my life and thought it nicer
Than what he had. Yet what he'd had seemed fine.
He'd never caught his fingers in the slicer
The way I'd managed in that life of mine.

His life lay glistening in the rain, neglected,
Yet still a decent, an authentic life.
Some people I can think of, I reflected
Would take that thing as soon as you'd say Knife.

It seemed a shame to miss a chance like that.
I brought the life in, dried it by the stove.
It looked so fetching, stretched out on the mat.
I tried it on. It fitted, like a glove.

And now, when some local bat drops off the twig
And new folk take the house, and pull up floors
And knock down walls and hire some kind of big
Container (say, a skip) for their old doors,

I'll watch it like a hawk, and every day
I'll make at least – oh – half a dozen trips.
I've furnished an existence in that way.
You'd not believe the things you find on skips.

James Fenton

■ In Transit ■

1. The Young Soldiers

Two weeks each of them has been away from home,
having a man made of him. In the legend
of small brothers. Behind reminiscence
in the Public Bar. And two days, a figure
home on leave. Arms linked, the girls in the Disco
cross the floor in threes: hello, they say, stranger.

Strange to be anyone, invisibility
at the back of the class retained them so long.
Strange as their exchange of nowhere for nowhere,
out of work on the streets of Bolton and Colne
or well-paid patrolling the streets of Belfast.
They talk vaguely of a tour in Germany.

They think over and over of coming out
with a trade. The train removes them south once more
for combat training. Now they are drinking like
troopers; and it could be because they are half-cut
they're telling you this, their hands shake and they are
crying. In the same breath keeled over asleep.

Roger Garfitt

Three Weeks to Argentina

Shall I wave my little
Union Jack?
Shall I go all out for
a big attack?
Shall I sing: 'My country
right or wrong!'?
Shall I rattle out a
sabre song?

Or shall I write of
sailor boys
deep in the sea, that can
make no noise?
Or of feckless, careless
young marines
missed by the girls
and the wet canteens?

It's hard for an old man
who's seen wars,
to welcome that devil
and his claws.
They reach from the ocean,
clash in the sky,
make the earth into
a shepherd's pie.

Professionals love it,
the admirals all,
a chance to show that they're
on the ball.
Newsmen like it,
because it's news –
but fathers and mothers
have different views.

Gavin Ewart
(17 April 1982)

Juan Lopez and John Ward

It was their fate to live in a strange time.
The planet had been carved into different countries,
each one provided with loyalties, with loved memories,
with a past which doubtless had been heroic, with
ancient and recent traditions, with rights, with grievances,
with its own mythology, with
forebears in bronze, with anniversaries, with demagogues and
with symbols.
Such an arbitrary division was favourable to war.

Lopez had been born in the city next to the motionless
river; Ward, in the outskirts of the city
through which
Father Brown had walked. He had studied Spanish so as
to read the Quixote.
The other professed a love of Conrad, revealed
to him in a class in Viamonte Street.
They might have been friends, but they saw each other just once,
face to face, in islands only too well-known,
and each one was Cain, and each one, Abel.
They buried them together. Snow and corruption
know them.
The story I tell happened in a time we cannot understand.

Jorge Luis Borges

■ Driving to a Death ■

I know these big arterial roads
pretty well now, how the wind
swings over bridges, kestrels simmer
on their hob, the crows time
near extinction to a hop, a step;
know the xerox smell as, heating
up, my car prints out the miles.

I stop as dusk comes on, fill up
and eat my tepid rolls. The coffee's
mashed itself to ashes. Zombies
keep a thin arm deep in pockets
and their brothers stamp my cheque.

Malvern and Cotswold go by
like darkening ancient liners.
North to south's no problem.
It's getting across country
to my birthplace: what connects
this road and that? I wind my way
across the plain; dark thatches
every mile until I hit the flyover
and lights seed their old magic
on Southampton Water, swaying oily hips
up at the lamps' cortege.

I speed past into the city suburbs,
limbs like armour, all the shires
packed humming in my head.
The gold watch that I bought
in Curacao is fastened to your speckly
wrist, turning heirloom by the hour.

William Scammell

From the Frontier of Writing

The tightness and the nilness round that space
when the car stops in the road, the troops inspect
its make and number and, as one bends his face

towards your window, you catch sight of more
on a hill beyond, eyeing with intent
down cradled guns that hold you under cover

and everything is pure interrogation
until a rifle motions and you move
with guarded unconcerned acceleration –

a little emptier, a little spent
as always by that quiver in the self,
subjugated, yes, and obedient.

So you drive on to the frontier of writing
where it happens again. The guns on tripods;
the sergeant with his on-off mike repeating

data about you, waiting for the squawk
of clearance; the marksman training down
out of the sun upon you like a hawk.

And suddenly you're through, arraigned yet freed,
as if you'd passed from behind a waterfall
on the black current of a tarmac road

past armour-plated vehicles, out between
the posted soldiers flowing and receding
like tree shadows into the polished windscreen.

Seamus Heaney

■ Green Beret ■

(Ho Thien of the 4th Plains Unit wrote this down sixty days after New Year, after hearing the story from a woman of Dalat on the High Plateau.)

He was twelve years old,
and I do not know his name.
The mercenaries took him and his father,
whose name I do not know,
one morning upon the High Plateau.
Green Beret looked down on the frail boy
with the eyes of a hurt animal and thought,
a good fright will make him talk.
He commanded, and the father was taken away
behind the forest's green wall.
'Right kid tell us where they are,
tell us where or your father – dead.'
With eyes now bright and filled with terror
the slight boy said nothing.
'You've got one minute left kid,' said Green Beret,
'tell us where or we kill father,'
and thrust his wristwatch against a face all eyes,
the second hand turning, jerking on its way.
'OK boy ten seconds to tell us where they are.'
In the last instant the silver hand shattered the sky and the forest
 of trees.
'Kill the old guy,' roared Green Beret
and shots hammered out
behind the forest's green wall
and sky and trees and soldiers stood
in silence, as the boy crouched down
and shook with tears,
as children do when their father dies.
'Christ,' said one mercenary to Green Beret,
'he didn't know a damn thing
we killed the old guy for nothing.'
So they all went away,
Green Beret and his mercenaries.

And the boy knew everything,
He knew everything about them, the caves,
the trails, the hidden places and the names,
and in the moment that he cried out
in that same instant,
protected by frail tears
far stronger than any wall of steel,
they passed everywhere
like tigers
across the High Plateau.

Ho Thien

Poem at Thirty-nine

How I miss my father.
I wish he had not been
so tired
when I was
born.

Writing deposit slips and checks
I think of him.
He taught me how.
This is the form,
he must have said:
the way it is done.
I learned to see
bits of paper
as a way
to escape
the life he knew
and even in high school
had a savings
account.

He taught me
that telling the truth
did not always mean
a beating;
though many of my truths
must have grieved him
before the end.

How I miss my father!
He cooked like a person
dancing
in a yoga meditation
and craved the voluptuous
sharing
of good food.

Now I look and cook just like him:
my brain light;
tossing this and that
into the pot;
seasoning none of my life
the same way twice; happy to feed
whoever strays my way.

He would have grown
to admire
the woman I've become:
cooking, writing, chopping wood,
staring into the fire.

Alice Walker

First Ice

A girl freezes in a telephone booth.
In her draughty overcoat she hides
A face all smeared
In tears and lipstick.

She breathes on her thin palms.
Her fingers are icy. She wears earrings.

She'll have to go home, alone,
Along the icy street.

First ice. It is the first time.
The first ice of telephone phrases.

Frozen tears glitter on her cheeks –
The first ice of human hurt.

Andre Voznesensky

■ First Frost ■

A girl is freezing in a telephone booth,
huddled in her flimsy coat,
her face stained by tears
and smeared with lipstick.

She breathes on her thin little fingers.
Fingers like ice. Glass beads in her ears.
She has to beat her way back alone
down the icy street.

First frost. A beginning of losses.
The first frost of telephone phrases.

It is the start of winter glittering on her cheek,
the first frost of having been hurt.

Andre Voznesensky

The Cleaner

I've seen it all, you know. Men.
Well, I've been married for thirty-two years,
I can do without them.
I know what they're after.

And these students. They're young, you know.
They don't know what it's all about,
The first years. And these post-grads;
I know what they're after.

They're older, you know. And by Christmas
They've finished here, they've gone. A girl
Can get hurt. I've been here eight years.
I've seen it happen.

Sometimes I say to a friend
You ought to talk to her. Does she know
What she's doing? And the friend'll say
Yes, she does know. Well, I hope I did right.

No need for any of 'em to have a baby,
But do they know? I feel a mother, like.
Once I did ask. I said *Do you know*
And she said *O yes, we know how far we're going.*

But these post-grads are older,
They take advantage. These girls, mind,
They're not all as innocent as you'd think.
Twenty stubs in the ashtray.

I can tell a lot from that.

U.A. Fanthorpe

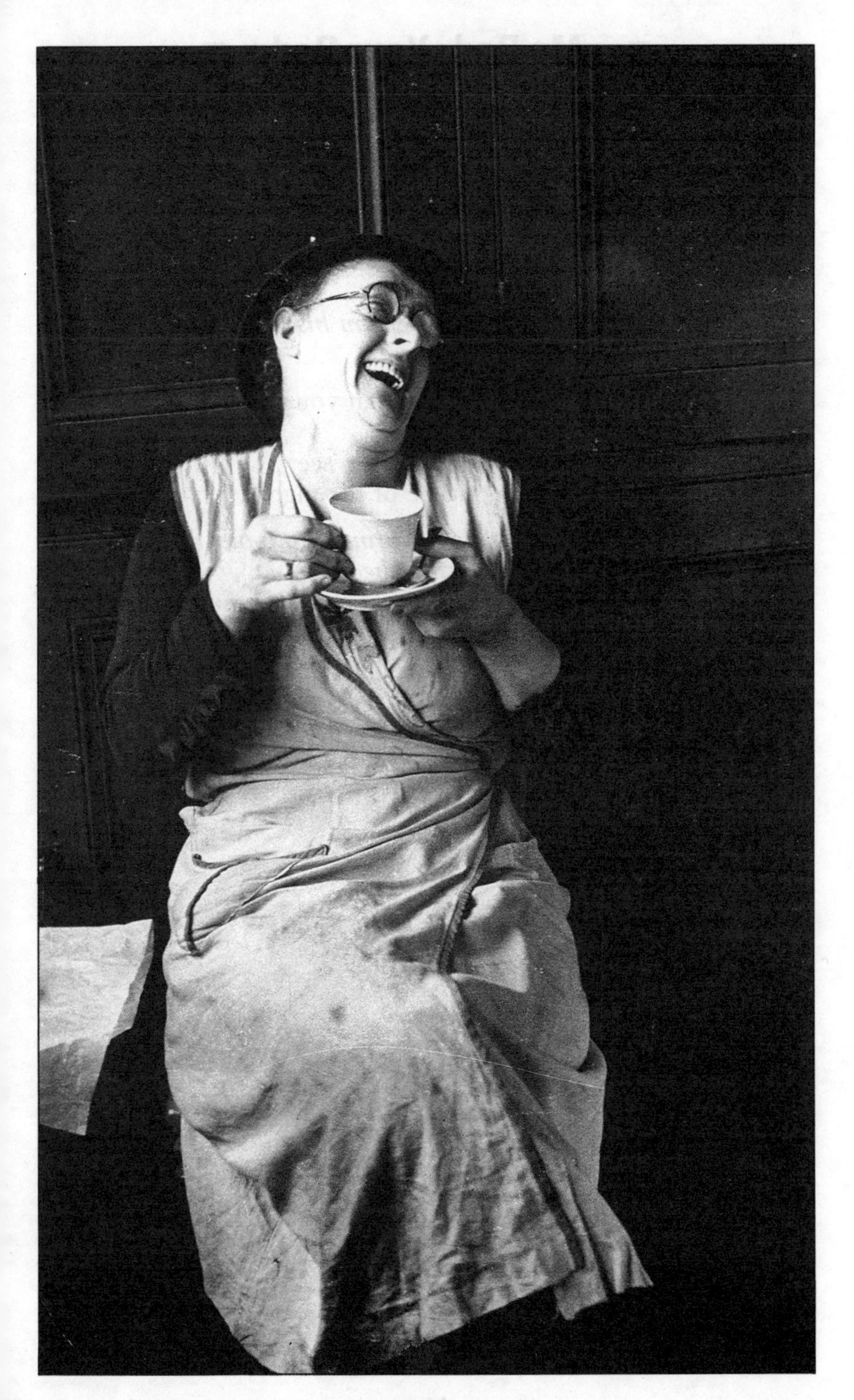

■ My Dad, Your Dad ■

My dad's fatter than your dad,
Yes, my dad's fatter than yours:
If he eats any more he won't fit in the house,
He'll have to live out of doors.

Yes, but my dad's balder than your dad,
My dad's balder, O.K.,
He's only got two hairs left on his head
And both are turning grey.

Ah, but my dad's thicker than your dad,
My dad's thicker, all right.
He has to look at his watch to see
If it's noon or the middle of the night.

Yes, but my dad's more boring than your dad.
If he ever starts counting sheep
When he can't get to sleep at night, he finds
It's the sheep that go to sleep.

But my dad doesn't mind your dad.
Mine quite likes yours too.
I suppose they don't always think much of US!
That's true, I suppose, that's true.

Kit Wright

■ Woodwork ■

On winter nights my father worked in wood.
Coke sighed and crackled in the rayburn,
dusty cats lay limp with heat,
home service voices spoke to us.
I watched the slow lead pencil trace
elaborate blueprints of his mind.
He measured, marked,
he stroked the surface of the wood,
touching the edges of his table
as if it was already there.

Sticking at first the saw would settle
to a regular raucous breathing, in and out.
The gritty rub of sandpaper,
the plane's sharp blade
sent falling drifts of pale sweet sawdust,
brittle ringlets of creamy wood.
Each cigarette's slow crumble into ash
became a scattering of soft grey flakes,
unnoticed.

Forgotten in his vision
I watched the quiet births of trolleys, tables, trays,
I watched his singlemindedness, his dreams.
He absorbed me in his concentration,
unknown to him it wrapped me round,
sheltered me from night time
and the cold dark house beyond that room.

Cynthia Fuller

The Hitch-Hiker

One hand crabs along the seat back,
prising a grip; one sensory foot
hovers down, testing the floor,
testing the temperature. He hangs
over the seat, as over a piping bath,
inching himself down.

There's a knife-edge brim on his old felt,
his muffler ties as neatly as silk:
of his natty dress, only the skills remain.
Nothing else's quite right: a hold-all for shopping,
trousers frayed at the knee. Old vanities
are the best he can do.

Alone at a bus stop, on the verge of the by-pass:
these are the Home Counties of the Moon. The present
starves him in its thin atmosphere. Death
is coming over him like a yawn.
He hitched a lift, his admission of exile
a shy elocution of the thumb.

He's talked himself down to the seat.
He muffs the door shut. I edge into gear
as he perches there, brittle, hollow-boned.
He settles back, and identity rises in him
– he's got his second wind. He remarks,
'You're nowhere without a car these days, are you?'

Roger Garfitt

Song of the Wagon Driver

My first love was the ten-ton truck
they gave me when I started,
and though she played the bitch with me
I grieved when we were parted.

Since then I've had a dozen more,
the wound was quick to heal,
and now it's easier to say
I'm married to my wheel.

I've trunked it north, I've trunked it south,
on wagons good and bad,
but none was ever really like
the first I ever had.

The life is hard, the hours are long,
sometimes I cease to feel,
but I go on, for it seems to me
I'm married to my wheel.

Often I think of my home and kids,
out on the road at night,
and think of taking a local job
provided the money's right.

Two nights a week I see my wife,
and eat a decent meal
but otherwise, for all my life,
I'm married to my wheel.

B.S. Johnson

■ The Rovers ■

My Dad, he wears a Rovers' scarf,
He wears a Rovers' cap,
And every Saturday before
He goes to see them fail to score,
He sighs, 'Oh no!
Why *do* I go?
They haven't got –
They've really not –
A rat's chance in a trap!'

And sure enough
They always stuff
The Rovers.

My Dad, he wears a Rovers' tie,
Two huge rosettes as well,
And every time before he leaves
He sits and hangs his head and grieves:
'I must be mad –
They're just so BAD!
They haven't got –
They've really not –
A snowball's hope in hell!'

And sure enough
They always stuff
The Rovers.

Rovers' ribbon, Rovers' rattle,
Dad takes when he's off to battle:
Shouts and stamps and stomps and rants.
DAD'S GOT ROVERS' UNDERPANTS!

Rovers' eyes!
Rovers' nose!
Rovers' elbows!
Off he goes

And sure enough
They always stuff
The Rovers.

EXCEPT
One glorious day,
It didn't work that way . . .
This was the state of play . . .

A goalless draw,
But just before
The final whistle went,
Rovers stole
The only goal:
I can't say it was *meant*:

What happened was
A wobbling cross
Back-bounced off someone's bum –
And Praise the Lord!
Rovers scored!
They'd won! Their hour had come!

So Dad, he whirled his Rovers' scarf,
He hurled his cap up high.
'Oh, we're the best there's ever been!
We're magic!' he yelled out. 'You've seen
Nothing yet.
Just wait. We're set!
Yes, you can bet
The lads will get
Promotion by and by!

Our luck is in –
We're *bound* to win –
Us Rovers!'

It didn't work that way,
Alas for Dad.
That goal's the only goal
They've ever had.

Now every Saturday before
He goes to see them lose once more,
He sighs, 'Oh no!
Why *do* I go?
They've got a curse –
They're getting *worse* –
How *can* they be so bad?'

And sure enough
They always
STUFF THE ROVERS!

Kit Wright

■ Looking for Dad ■

Whenever Mum and Dad
were full of gloom
they always yelled,
'TIDY UP YOUR ROOM!'
Just because my comics were
scattered here and
everywhere and
because I did not care
where I left my underwear
they yelled: 'WE'LL SEND YOU TO
A HOUSE OF CORRECTION
IF YOU DON'T TIDY UP
YOUR STAMP COLLECTION!'
Then one day they
could not care less
about the room's
awful mess.
They seemed more intent
on a domestic argument.
They both looked glum
and instead of me Dad
screeched at Mum.
One night when I
went to bed he
simply vanished.
(Ten past seven, tenth of June.)
I had not tidied
up my room because
I too was
full of gloom.
That night I dreamt
Dad was hidden
beneath the things
I'd been given.
In my dream
I was in despair
and flung about my underwear
but could not find
him anywhere.

I looked for him
lots and lots
beneath crumpled sheets
and old robots.
I looked in cupboards
and in shoes.
I looked up all
the chimney flues.
I remembered how
he'd seemed to be
unhappier than
even me. When I woke I knew
it was not my room
that filled Mum and Dad
with so much gloom.
Now I stare at all
my old toy cars
and carpets stained
with old Mars bars
and hope he will
come back soon
and admire my very tidy room.
(It is now the twenty-ninth of June.)

Brian Patten

■ Login ■

Chapel and bridge. A headlong fall
into woods. A river running fast
divides the wild cow parsley.
'My father lived here once,' I said,
'I think you knew him.'

The sun, hot at our backs, whitens
the lane. She, in shadow, allows
the sun to pass her into the passage.
I gain entry at his name, tea,
a lace cloth on the table.

When talking is done she ruffles
my son's brown hair with a hand
that is bruised with age. Veins stand,
fast water in her wrists. Handshakes,
glances converging could not span
such giddy water.

Out in the lane the thrush outsings
the river. The village is at lunch.
The bridge burns with cow parsley.
We stand in the brilliance without words,
watch him running into the light.

Should he turn now to wave and wait
for me, where sunlight concentrates
blindingly on the bridge, he'd see
all this in sepia, hear footsteps
not yet taken fade away.

Gillian Clarke

Finding a Sheep's Skull

Sudden shock of bone
at the path's edge,
like a larger mushroom
almost hidden by leaves,

I handle the skull gently
shaking out earth and spiders.
Loose teeth chock in the jaw:
it smells of nothing.

I hold it up to sunlight,
a grey-green translucent shell.
Light pours in
like water
through blades and wafers of bone.
In secret caves
filaments of skull hang down;
frost and rain have worked
to shredded lace.

The seasons waste its symmetry.
It is a cathedral
echoing spring; in its decay
plainsong of lamb
and field and sun
inhabits bone.

The shallow cranium
fits in my palm

– for speculative children
I bring it home.

Frances Horovitz

■ Follower ■

My father worked with a horse-plough,
His shoulders globed like a full sail strung
Between the shafts and the furrow.
The horses strained at his clicking tongue.

An expert. He would set the wing
And fit the bright steel-pointed sock.
The sod rolled over without breaking.
At the headrig, with a single pluck

Of reins, the sweating team turned round
And back into the land. His eye
Narrowed and angled at the ground,
Mapping the furrow exactly.

I stumbled in his hob-nailed wake,
Fell sometimes on the polished sod;
Sometimes he rode me on his back
Dipping and rising to his plod.

I wanted to grow up and plough,
To close one eye, stiffen my arm.
All I ever did was follow
In his broad shadow round the farm.

I was a nuisance, tripping, falling,
Yapping always. But today
It is my father who keeps stumbling
Behind me, and will not go away.

Seamus Heaney

■ Quiet Eyes ■

Please don't mind, Grandad, if I stay at home today
but I'd rather lie in bed and close my eyes,

remembering the way you twirled your shiny shoe
when you taught me out-swing corners in the park,

and your eyes grew strong and dreamy
when you told how Plantaganet, your horse,

stopped his cart outside the Cholmondely Arms
until you bought a gill of bitter, in a pail.

You see, we did cremations in Joan of Arc
at school. I couldn't bear to see your eyes

when the undertaker slides you from the coffin,
ropes you to the stake and strikes a match.

How can they watch you bravely burning
– kneeling round you on their hassocks

singing 'Onward Christian Soldiers',
while the purple music squeezes on your ears?

I want you with me at the bottom of the garden
in the soft sun before the dark,

measuring my height against your buttons
– last month, I'd only three to go.

When I told you that your eyes looked tired
and asked you if you would die, you were quiet

for a while, then squeezed my knee. 'Not before
you score left-footed for West Brom,' you said.

I know the flames can't hurt – you're like Shadrach
and those other men you sang to me about.

But you won't feel easy in the holy smoke
until it's so thick that they can't see you.

Then you'll loosen your bone collar-stud again.
But those eyes, Grandad. Those quiet eyes.

Are you wearing your best waistcoat
with a bag of all-sorts in your secret pocket?

John Latham

■ Old Father ■

Old Father to England in Winter '59.
Cold bite him hard,
Make him bawl in his small basement room
By the Grove.
Every day he cry out:
'Man, a tekkin' de nex' boat back home.'
But come spring,
Old Father still here.

Time passed.
Old Father feet begin to shift.
His roots have no meaning now.
He straighten his hair,
Press it smooth.
Coloured girls no good for he –
Day after day you see him
Bouncing down the road with a blonde,
Never brunette,
And his suit, cream or beige,
Never anything dark.

Old Father don't mix with the boys
On Saturday night no more –
No, he sit in the pub up the road –
The one at the corner
That don't like serving black people –
And he crack joke with them white people on we.
'Tut tut,' he would say,
'Isn't it disgusting
How they make a spectacle of themselves
At cricket matches.'

He don't say 'Hello' no more,
Don't eat dasheen or yam –
'not very digestible' –
And Heaven forbid,
He even turn his back on
Saltfish with 'chove an' dumpling.

Boy,
Old Father don't want to know we now,
In his white Rover,
With his slicked-back hair.
And them white people saying
'He's an example to his people.'

Hugh Boatswain

■ Bedtime Stories ■

At night we were wanderers
through a world of words

Travelling for the love of it
we would never hesitate
to stop and look around us
change direction
start afresh

Together we walked the main roads
and the less trod paths:
With him I learned
to use the signposts
read the maps

We were company

But I became impatient
discovered the thrill of speed
rejected his slow
unfolding of words
with all the extra meaning it could bring

I wanted to set my own pace
plan my own route

Slowly we drifted apart
went our separate ways
we travelled together
less often
and then not at all

I became a solitary explorer

journeyed far and journeyed fast
missed much
saw much

made my own way

He reads to my sister now
and sometimes
a world-weary nomad
I sneak into her room
and lie curled up on the floor

in companionable silence

Jenny Moy

■ Long Distance II ■

Though my mother was already two years dead
Dad kept her slippers warming by the gas,
put hot water bottles her side of the bed
and still went to renew her transport pass.

You couldn't just drop in. You had to phone.
He'd put you off an hour to give him time
To clear away her things and look alone
as though his still raw love were such a crime.

He couldn't risk my blight of disbelief
though sure that very soon he'd hear her key
scrape in the rusted lock and end his grief.
He *knew* she'd just popped out to get the tea.

I believe life ends with death, and that is all.
You haven't both gone shopping; just the same,
in my new black leather phone book there's your name
and the disconnected number I still call.

Tony Harrison

A Roadside Feast

He slaps the hedgehog off the road
He chivvies it off with scraping prongs
He pins it alive on metal points
The blood catches the starlight
He says you must watch for fleas and not touch this vermin
He prods it down in the bank of clay
He stirs it round until it is an earth ball
Taking a twig he scrapes it off
Into the heart of the fire where it glows
And sizzles like a speeding cannonball
A high-pitched cry of juice from a blowhole
With his trowel he dibbles it out on a stone
Taps it and cracks it, the clay shards-off
He pulls them with scalding fingers
A roasting smell pays attention, we lean forward,
Like a six inch pig the naked food
Glorious with grease. He waves us off
Bake you own hedge-pig, he says.
I pick up a shard, daggered with long pins.

Peter Redgrove

▪ The Mirror ▪

In memory of my father

I

He was no longer my father
but I was still his son;
I would get to grips with that cold paradox,
the remote figure in his Sunday best
who was buried the next day.

A great day for tears, snifters of sherry,
whiskey, beef sandwiches, tea.
An old mate of his was recounting
their day excursion
to Youghal in the Thirties,
how he was his first partner
on the Cork/Skibbereen route
in the late Forties.
There was a splay of Mass cards
on the sitting-room mantelpiece
which formed a crescent round a glass vase,
his retirement present from C.I.E.

II

I didn't realize till two days later
it was the mirror took his breath away.

The monstrous old Victorian mirror
with the ornate gilt frame
we had found in the three-storey house
when we moved in from the country.
I was afraid that it would sneak
down from the wall and swallow me up
in one gulp in the middle of the night.

While he was decorating the bedroom
he had taken down the mirror
without asking for help;
soon he turned the colour of terracotta
and his heart broke that night.

III

There was nothing for it
but to set about finishing the job,
papering over the cracks,
painting the high window,
stripping the door, like the door of a crypt.
When I took hold of the mirror
I had a fright. I imagined him breathing through it.
I heard him say in a reassuring whisper:
I'll give you a hand, here.

And we lifted the mirror back in position
above the fireplace,
my father holding it steady
while I drove home
the two nails.

Paul Muldoon
(from the Irish of Michael Davitt)

■ Sons ■

When they are late sometimes
slow minutes, darkness, the traffic's roar
open a crack upon the fear of losing them –
the world turned grey, the silence.
And when the one or other enters
innocent of time or danger,
I must not hold him tightly as I would,
nor trace the outline of his face,
nor search his eyes for who he is.

It is not the darkness nor the danger
that will take them.
They are beginning to cross over now,
round bodies pared to a taut skinniness,
longlegged, angular, they move
with conscious carelessness, defended.
Afraid for them, for me,
I watch them leaving
for a world I cannot comprehend.

Is there some charm that I can give them,
some gentle amulet to see them safe across,
to let me loose them and to let them choose
sometimes to come back.

Cynthia Fuller

■ Hit! ■

I raise my hand against my son
And all night afterwards re-run

A bitter sequence in my head.
That hand is not this hand. Instead

Of this hand rising in the light
That hand is rough, the knuckles white

Where skin is tight across the bone.
This hand is not that hand. My own

Is long and delicate. The fists,
As skinny as a Lazarist's,

Are bony; not so quick, so square.
That hand is not this hand but where

The fingers rise against the brain
I feel again that shock, that pain

Of snap rejection. Now I know
This hand becomes that hand. I grow

More like my father on whose grave
The ragged grasses misbehave.

Pete Morgan

■ The Funeral of Father ■

Black,
They all wore black.
Even the cat wore black.

Flowers.
Wreaths of flowers.
Gardens of flowers
for him who only grew vegetables.
Mother.
Mother wept
forgetting the black eyes he gave her
And brother,
my brother didn't care
to remember the beatings.
Only I spat on the coffin
as it dropped
and said something
my sister wouldn't tell the vicar,
who, while reading the service,
scratched his nose.
And that was the end of Father.

Back home we drank
the sherry from under the stairs.
Aunt Flo remembered early years
when Father was a lad.
I smiled,
infamous by now
for my lack of gravity.
I smiled and said aloud,
'He was the biggest bastard
you ever knew,'
and then,
as the clock passed one,
they had an honest moment;
but nobody denounced
the prodigal son
with his two-tone shoes.
That was the memory of Father.

Denise King

DADDY
SCHOOL

1113 Park Avenue

Every door was closed.
The blinds were taut against the sun
and the children all in place
except the son they'd sent away.

The mother lay
in a room at the back of the house
knowing it no longer mattered,
chain smoking,
flipping through the fashion magazines
and listening
to the hum of the air conditioner.

It fell to the eldest daughter
to turn it off.
Sweating slightly in her tennis whites,
she opened all the blinds
on the day her mother died.

Alice Kavounas

■ The Flowers ■

After lunch my daughter picked
handfuls of the wild flowers
she knew her grandfather liked best
and piled them in the basket of her bicycle,
beside an empty jam-jar and a trowel;
then, swaying like a candle-bearer,
she rode off to the church
and, like a little dog, I followed her.

She cleared the grave of nettles
and wild parsley, and dug a shallow hole
to put the jam-jar in. She arranged
the flowers to look their best
and scraped the moss from the stone,
so you could see whose grave
she had been caring for.
It didn't take her long – no longer
than making his bed in the morning
when he had got too old to help her.

Not knowing how to leave him,
how to say good-bye, I hesitated
by the rounded grave. *Come on*,
my daughter said, *It's finished now*.
And so we got our bicycles and rode home
down the lane, moving apart
and coming together again,
in and out of the ruts.

Selima Hill

Country Afternoon

we buy postcards
sepia-tinted
putting extra money, carefully, in the box

a lone tourist
made nervous by laughter
and the child climbing on tombstones
hurries towards the lych-gate
shuts it with an echoing click

a church noted by Betjeman
saddle-backed, herring-boned
tiny, cool
more ancient than its written history
a god's eye in Cotswold fields:
outside, the graven cross, six centuries worn
is a single shaft to heaven

from the crypt I look up
see your face for an instant
dark against sunlight
still as a stone knight

a wood-pigeon clatters –
from a smouldering bonfire
smoke wavers upwards
we gaze into the rectory orchard
heavy with forbidden fruit
dahlias in shocks lean towards us

across the lane
five geese from a fairy tale
cows gathered peaceably to be milked
a muddy ford with minnows
no sound or sight of other human
fifteen adults in this community
a few children and the old
where are they all –
indoors, or vanished long ago
into the hedgerows, the rolling fields?

at the edge of the wood a horse chases a cow

'an afternoon out of time,' you say
'fifty years or more ago
– if I built a church it would be like this'

I pick flowers that will not last the journey home

heat dances on tarmac
the child runs towards the car

where to go from here?

Frances Horovitz

On Finding an Old Photograph

Yalding, 1912. My father
in an apple orchard, sunlight
patching his stylish bags;

three women dressed in soft,
white blouses, skirts that brush the grass;
a child with curly hair.

If they were strangers
it would calm me – half-drugged
by the atmosphere – but it does more –

eases a burden
made of all his sadness
and the things I didn't give him.

There he is, happy, and I am unborn.

Wendy Cope

Miracle on St. David's Day

'They flash upon that inward eye
Which is the bliss of solitude'
The Daffodils *by W. Wordsworth*

An afternoon yellow and open-mouthed
with daffodils. The sun treads the path
among cedars and enormous oaks.
It might be a country house, guests strolling,
the rumps of gardeners between nursery shrubs.

I am reading poetry to the insane.
An old woman, interrupting, offers
as many buckets of coal as I need.
A beautiful chestnut-haired boy listens
entirely absorbed. A schizophrenic

on a good day, they tell me later.
In a cage of first March sun a woman
sits not listening, not seeing, not feeling.
In her neat clothes the woman is absent.
A big, mild man is tenderly led

to his chair. He has never spoken.
His labourer's hands on his knees, he rocks
gently to the rhythms of the poems.
I read to their presences, absences,
to the big, dumb labouring man as he rocks.

He is suddenly standing, silently,
huge and mild, but I feel afraid. Like slow
movement of spring water or the first bird
of the year in the breaking darkness,
the labourer's voice recites 'The Daffodils'.

The nurses are frozen, alert; the patients
seem to listen. He is hoarse but word-perfect.
Outside the daffodils are still as wax,
a thousand, ten thousand, their syllables
unspoken, their creams and yellows still.

Forty years ago. in a Valleys school,
the class recited poetry by rote.
Since the dumbness of misery fell
he has remembered there was a music
of speech and that once he had something to say.

When he's done, before the applause, we observe
the flowers' silence. A thrush sings
and the daffodils are flame.

Gillian Clarke

National Trust

Bottomless pits. There's one in Castleton,
and stout upholders of our law and order
one day thought its depth worth wagering on
and borrowed a convict hush-hush from his warder
and winched him down; and back, flayed, grey, mad, dumb.

Not even a good flogging made him holler!

O gentlemen, a better way to plumb
the depths of Britain's dangling a scholar,
say, here at the booming shaft at Towanroath,
now National Trust, a place where they got tin,
those gentlemen who silenced the men's oath
and killed the language that they swore it in.

The dumb go down in history and disappear
and not one gentleman's been brought to book:

Mes den hep tavas a-gollas y dyr

(Cornish) –
'the tongueless man gets his land took.'

Tony Harrison

■ Always a Suspect ■

I get up in the morning
and dress up like a gentleman –
A white shirt a tie and a suit

I walk into the street
to be met by a man
who tells me to 'produce'.
I show him
the document of my existence
to be scrutinised and given the nod.

Then I enter the foyer of a building
to have my way barred by a commissionaire.
'What do you want?'

I trudge the city pavements
side by side with 'madam'
who shifts her handbag
from my side to the other,
and looks at me with eyes that say
'Ha! Ha! I know who you are;
beneath those fine clothes
ticks the heart of a thief.'

Oswald Mbuyiseni Mtshali

The Fat Black Woman Goes Shopping

Shopping in London winter
is a real drag for the fat black woman
going from store to store
in search of accomodating clothes
and de weather so cold

Look at the frozen thin mannequins
fixing her with grin
and de pretty face salesgals
exchanging slimming glances
thinking she won't notice

Lord is aggravating

Nothing soft and bright and billowing
To flow like breezy sunlight
when she walking

The fat black woman curses in Swahili/Yoruba
and nation language under her breathing
all this journeying and journeying

The fat black woman could only conclude
that when it come to fashion
the choice is lean

Nothing much beyond size 14

Grace Nichols

TOP
NOTCH

■ Rainbow ■

When you see
de rainbow
you know
God know
wha he doing –
one big smile
across the sky –
I tell you God got style
the man got style

When you see
raincloud pass
and de rainbow
make a show
I tell you
is God doing
limbo
the man doing
limbo

But sometimes
you know
when I see
de rainbow
so full of glow
and curving
like she bearing child
I does want know
if God
ain't a woman

If that so
the woman got style
man she got style

John Agard

■ Sanctuary ■

Seagulls in a loose V-formation
Fly in squadrons over the estate
Westwards on winter evenings to the Severn.
The Estuary, no doubt. Mudflats at sunset.
Buffeted by winds the seagulls rally.
Caught by the rain they hold their courses firm.
Tinted by sunlight they move comfortably,
And every evening I look up to them
As fly-pasts for the men returning home.

Duncan Forbes

■ My Box ■

My box is made of golden oak,
my lover's gift to me.
He fitted hinges and a lock
of brass and a bright key.
He made it out of winter nights,
sanded and oiled and planed,
engraved inside the heavy lid
in brass, a golden tree.

In my box are twelve black books
where I have written down
how we have sanded, oiled and planed,
planted a garden, built a wall,
seen jays and goldcrests, rare red kites,
found the wild heartsease, drilled a well,
harvested apples and words and days
and planted a golden tree.

On an open shelf I keep my box.
Its key is in the lock.
I leave it there for you to read,
or them, when we are dead,
how everything is slowly made,
how slowly things made me,
a tree, a lover, words, a box,
books and a golden tree.

Gillian Clarke

Follow on

■ To the teacher ■

In the Introduction to *Wordlife* some general principles were proposed about how to take poetry into the classroom. This section is designed to suggest more specific activities. For obvious reasons, a distinction has been drawn between work that depends upon the teacher, and work which students can undertake on their own initiative. Talking in small groups, for example, almost always depends upon the presence of a teacher to get things going. A 'reading log', on the other hand, needs privacy and time for reflection. Both, however, are necessary, and complementary, elements in a total approach to poetry and it should not be thought that one is being given precedence over the other.

Starting points

The circumstances under which poetry is shared with pupils should be:

- as varied as possible
- not merely fitting a pre-determined theme
- not mechanistic.

The pupils' initial responses to the sound, the rhythm, the poet's feelings and the language in which they are expressed, are all important.

1. Poems should be read aloud, particularly where the impact will be powerful. In this anthology, 'He Always . . .' (p. 24), 'National Trust' (p. 80), 'Long Distance II' (p. 64) and 'Miracle on St. David's Day' (p. 78), amongst others, make a very striking first impression. 'Christmas Thankyou's' (p. 12), too, benefits from an adult reading it aloud.

2. Discussion around, rather than about, the text can often provide a manageable starting point that pays dividends later. In *Teaching Poetry in the Secondary School*, HMI describe an oblique approach in which Hardy's 'The Self-Unseeing' is explored by the pupils looking at family anecdote and reminiscence.

3. *Tray* is a computer program which enables the pupil, collaborating in a small group, to 'sidle up on the text'. Devised originally with the slow reader in mind, the program is an invaluable tool for introducing poetry to pupils of all ages and abilities. Pupils begin with a blank screen (apart from the punctuation), or perhaps with part of the text revealed to them. Through their discussion and their predictions, the developing poem emerges on the screen.

```
Sea u  s  n       se  - r at  n
  y in squadr ns   er the estate
Westwards  n w nter e en n s t  the Severn.
The Estuary, n  d u t.   ud  ats at sunset.
u  eted  y w nds the sea u  s ra  y.

 au ht  y the ra n they h  d the r  urses   r .
T nted  y sun    ht they   e   rta  y,
And e ery e en n         k u  t  the
As   y- asts   r the  en return n  h  e.
```

This shows the activity at a critical point: at the moment when the attention of the pupils should be moving away from the relationship between letters and on to determining the overall meaning of the poem.

In this example, Duncan Forbes' poem 'Sanctuary' (p. 85) is used. The title of the poem has been concealed from the pupils in order to stimulate further discussion. Other poems in *Wordlife* that particularly lend themselves to this way of working include:

- 'Hit!' by Pete Morgan (p. 69)
- 'First Ice' by Andre Voznesensky (p. 40)

Probably the biggest constraint is the screen itself; only text up to a certain size is suitable!

4. Textual work of this kind does not depend upon having a computer in the room. Using more orthodox techniques, it is quite possible to provoke discussion, either with the class as a whole or in small groups, by concealing part of the text in order to set problems. Success depends upon whether the teacher is able to match the right technique to the right poem and whether the pupils feel that the problems are worth solving. Examples of how this might work in practice include:
   - Speculating from the title what the poem might be about, e.g. 'Finding a Sheep's Skull' (p. 55)
   - Providing the title (on an OHP) and releasing the poem line by line, e.g. 'A Roadside Feast' (p. 65)
   - Sharing the poem with the last line omitted, e.g. 'Tich Miller' (p. 1)
   - Concealing the title in order to allow the class to devise their own, e.g. 'The Choosing' (p. 22) and 'Follower' (p. 56).
5. Many of the approaches being advocated above will be familiar as DARTS (Directed Activities Related to Texts). The chart overleaf provides a brief summary of the kinds of activity that are usually indicated by this term.

Directed Activities Related to Texts	Poems
1 Deletion a) *Cloze* Children discuss the most appropriate word to fit a gap left in the text, either a random gap or, say, every 6th word. The word(s) negotiated should make sense, be 'grammatical' and fit in terms of style. b) *Variations* • Delete larger blocks of text. • Compare versions with other groups and with the original.	'Follower' (p. 56) 'For Adam, Nearly Twelve' (p. 11) 'Sanctuary' (p. 85) 'First Ice'/'First Frost' (pp. 40–41) 'Finding a Sheep's Skull' (p. 55)
2 Questions a) *Open rather than closed* Open questions (e.g. Why choose this title? What has the writer left out?) demand thought, provoke argument and alter traditional views about the relationship between reader and text. b) *Pupils' questions* In pairs or threes, children devise questions on the text, perhaps in character.	
3 Sequencing In small groups, the children are given a prose extract or a poem cut into lines, segments or even individual words. By careful reading – and re-reading – the group decides on an acceptable order. This works particularly well with verse.	'Green Beret' (p. 36) 'Quiet Eyes' (p. 58) 'The Face of Hunger' (p. 7) 'Rainbow' (p. 84)
4 Prediction The pupils, from their knowledge of a text, predict what is going to happen next. This works well as an activity for the whole class with the teacher releasing text line by line, or section by section, using an OHP.	'A Roadside Feast' (p. 65) 'Tich Miller' (p. 1) 'Driving to a Death' (p. 33) 'Looking for Dad' (p. 52)
5 Analysing text Pupils are asked to underline, label or 'segment' text, for a specific purpose.	'Old Father' (p. 60) 'He Always . . .' (p. 24)
6 Visual representation of text After reading the text, pupils may draw maps, diagrams or complete tables – after due discussion.	
What size groups? What kinds of text? What kind of talk occurs in the group? When is a particular strategy appropriate? What are the benefits?	

A word of warning, though, should accompany this chart. DARTS need to be handled with care and sensitivity. They can destroy the pupil's sense of the poem as a whole, replacing it with isolated fragments of language. And used with poetry, there is always a danger that they will inhibit, rather than encourage, a felt 'response'. Arguably DARTS works best:

- in smaller groups (two or three)
- when the activity fits into a broader context, i.e. when the text is not chosen at random
- when the children understand that their response is not 'right' or 'wrong'
- when the text fits the DART and both fit the group
- when the strategy remains secondary to the text.

It is essential that, at some point, the focus is shifted back to the whole poem: it needs reconstructing and the best, most logical way of doing that is to read it aloud.

In finished form

'In finished form' is intended to suggest that the poems themselves should, sooner or later, be studied as complete finished texts. By focussing on product rather than on process, it suggests a clear contrast with the earlier 'follow on' work. This section provides different kinds of activities that go beyond previous exploratory encounters with the poems and encourages pupils to craft their own responses in a more considered form.

Traditionally, of course, the pupil's considered response has always been couched in one familiar form – the literary critical essay. Whilst this kind of writing continues to have a place, it should not be forgotten that there are plenty of other ways in which a pupil, or a group of pupils, can demonstrate what they think and feel about a poem.

1 Using tape recorders

Activity	Suggestions	Poems
Taped reading	By an individual By a pair/group Can be exchanged with another class.	Selected by pupil(s)
Taped anthology	By a group for another audience: younger pupils parents old people.	'When you're a GROWN UP' (p. 10) 'Christmas Thankyou's' (p. 12)
Taped radio programme	On a theme About a poet	
Taped discussion	Without teacher intervention	

2 Using illustration

Activity	Suggestions	Poems
Poetry wall display	Devised by the class	
Photographs chosen to illustrate poems	Could be photographs taken by pupils	'Three weeks to Argentina' (p. 31)
Frieze or collage	Particularly suitable for narrative poems	
Posters		

3 Using drama

Activity	Suggestions	Poems
Presenting the poem in dramatic form	Small groups Time limit necessary	'Tich Miller' (p. 1) 'Always a Suspect' (p. 81)
Movement work or dance		
Enactment of the story behind the poem		'The Funeral of Father' (p. 70)
In the hot seat	Questioning of a character in the poem	'The Skip' (p. 27)

4 Using pen and paper

Activity	Suggestions	Poems
Parody or imitation		'The Rovers' (p. 48)
Developing the story	What happened before? Or after?	'The Skip' (p. 27) 'In Transit 1. The Young Soldiers' (p. 30)
Reworking it in a different form	As a playscript As a newspaper account	'Remembering St. Mary's Churchyard' (p. 18) 'Green Beret' (p. 36)
Exploring the situation	Interviewing the poet or character Diaries kept by characters	'The choosing' (p. 22) 'Old Father' (p. 60)
Formal writing about poetry	Allow formal writing to grow out of preparatory work, e.g. reading, note-making, drafting Comparison of different versions of the same poem	All poems 'First Ice'/'First Frost' (pp. 40-41)

Gareth Owen's implied advice in 'Miss Creedle Teaches Creative Writing' (p. 4) is worth heeding! Work with poetry should not be confined to the mechanistic. The advantage of using tape, illustrations and drama as well as writing, is that new media help us to think in new ways. However, they also make new demands. Most of the activities listed above can best be undertaken by pupils working in small groups, taking responsibility for their own work. That is the great advantage of structuring work around the creation of a finished product. Pupils, however, will not automatically be able to respond to this kind of challenge. They need to be taught the right kind of approach.

For a start, talking and writing should be closely inter-connected: pupils should talk in order to write; talk about what they are writing; and write from earlier discussion. Michael and Peter Benton's book *Examining Poetry: a Practical Guide for 15–18 year olds* is helpful here, identifying three activities to be done in sequence before writing begins. Even if the final version is a radio programme or a wall display rather than an essay, the message remains the same.

1 Reading
- silently, alone
- aloud in a group.

2 Notemaking
- scribbled around the poem . . .

3 Drafting
- using **1** and **2** to answer three questions:
  'What sort of poem is it?'
  'How does it work?'
  'How do I feel about it?'

Both of the first two questions presuppose some 'technical vocabulary': terms that describe features of poetry. The circumstances under which such metalanguage is introduced are important to get right. Technical terms should be taught naturally, through use, and not as lists of words to be learnt.

One way of doing this is to focus on the way in which a poem is crafted. For example, 'First Ice'/'First Frost' (pp. 40–41), distinct translations from the original Russian, offer an intriguing contrast and an opportunity for looking at the effects of individual words and syntax. It is worth getting half the class to look at 'First Frost' and the rest at 'First Ice'; the different effects of the translation can be discussed separately and then as a whole class. The focus can be made sharper by providing specific parallels: the words that describe the girl in the poem, for example, and the effect they create in the reader.

Another possibility is to use the word-processing facility on a microcomputer to edit and shape an early version of a poem. Activities like this can prepare pupils for working in groups to agree about how to devise, draft and polish whatever they have created, be it a commentary, a poster, a drama or an anthology.

Making poetry

Some years ago, a contributor to *NATENEWS* penned the following – presumably spoof – poetry 'assignment'. It should serve as a reminder to all of us about how not to do it!

> Make up a poem which shows one or more examples of ordinary, masculine, feminine and triple rhyme, assonance and consonance. It must also show examples of the use of similies (sic), metaphors, symbolism, onomatopoeia, imagery, irony, – and a pun if possible. Give the metre of your poem some thought and comment on the mood and tone of your poem . . . this will be difficult . . .

Taught well, poetry makes us aware of what we ourselves might do with language. It is logical, therefore, to expect that some pupils will want to be poets themselves. Encouraging this should be less a matter of prescription, 'Here are some poems which deal with the situation; now write one of your own . . .' and more of creating a confidence that writing poetry is a valid response, while ensuring that pupils are aware that poetry has form and power, and is not an easy, 'freewheeling' option.

One way of encouraging apprentice writers is to help them see how other people's poetry can serve as a 'trigger' for their own. The term is one used by John Foggin in *Write to the Point: Making a Poetry Anthology* which provides much useful guidance and many additional ideas. He cites 'Follower' (p. 56) as one poem which invites another. Other poems in this collection which might serve the same function include:

- 'Tich Miller' (p. 1)
- 'Three Weeks to Argentina' (p. 31)
- 'Song of the Wagon Driver' (p. 47)
- 'Old Father' (p. 60)
- 'Long Distance II' (p. 64)

John Foggin's advice on how teachers can best respond to pupils' poems, especially first drafts is also extremely helpful:

> . . . praise/blame value-judgements of writing are valueless. For the teacher in the first instance to say 'I like this – especially the bit where . . .' tends to stop any dialogue which may help the poem develop . . .

A more effective alternative is for pupils to learn to ask, of themselves and others, the right questions. The kinds of question, in other words, that will enable them to take their own poems forward under their own steam.

■ To the student ■

Making Poetry

'You have to inhabit poetry
if you want to make it.'

And what's 'to inhabit'?

To be in the habit of, to wear
words, sitting in the plainest light,
in the silk of morning, in the shoe of night;
a feeling, bare and frondish in surprising air;
familiar . . . rare.

And what's 'to make'?

To be and to become words' passing
weather; to serve a girl on terrible
terms, embark on voyages over voices,
evade the ego-hill, the misery-well,
the siren hiss of *publish, success, publish,*
success, success, success.
And why inhabit, make, inherit poetry?

Oh, it's the shared comedy of the worst
blessed; the sound leading the hand;
a wordlife running from mind to mind
through the washed rooms of the simple senses;
one of those haunted, undefendable, unpoetic
crosses we have to find.

Anne Stevenson

Starting points

If you are reading this, it is probably because you have been studying some of the poetry in *Wordlife* with your teacher. Whether you like it or loathe it, you will probably agree that poetry is different from other kinds of writing. Think, for example, about how you might read the back of a cereal packet over the breakfast table; you know immediately what it is saying. Even when you are reading a story, you do not often have to read the words more than once. Poetry is not quite so straightforward.

Because it takes longer to become familiar with a poem, it is important that, before anything else, you have a chance to work out for yourself what it is all about. There is no one right way of doing this; you need to devise an approach that suits you. You might, however, want to try out some of the ideas that follow.

Keeping a poetry journal

In some schools, it's quite usual for students to keep a private poetry journal. This is normally an exercise book that the teacher only sees if you choose to allow it. A book like this can be used to collect your first impressions of poems, and because it is a private piece of writing, you do not have to worry about spelling and punctuation as much as you normally would. Just feel free to write.

The first time you try this, you might find it a bit strange. You will probably be a little uncertain about what to write and what purpose it is serving. Remember that what the journal can help you do is to record all the thoughts that go through your head *as you are reading*. The following suggestions might be helpful:

Activity	Starting point	Advice	Poems
Put down your reactions.	'What it makes me think of is . . .'	Record your first impressions.	'National Trust' (p. 80) 'Rainbow' (p. 84)
	What picture does it conjure up?	Draw a sketch.	
	'That reminds me of . . .'	Jot down any memories of your own that have been triggered by the poem.	'On Finding an Old Photograph' (p. 76)
Ask questions.	'Why write . . .?' 'What's a . . .?'	Get the questions written down as quickly as you can before you forget them.	
Answer questions.	'It makes sense like this. . . .'	Use a phrase like this to get going and then keep going.	'My Box' (p. 86) 'Nightride' (p. 16)
Express a preference.	'The part I like best is . . .'	Copy down the words and phrases that you find most striking.	

If you want to try out some of these ideas for yourself, you could make a start with the poems suggested.

Other ways into a poem

If the idea of a journal does not appeal to you, there are other ways of finding your way into a poem. First a word of warning, though. Many of the ideas that follow require you to write on the page. In order not to spoil your copy of *Wordlife*, it would be advisable to print the poem out first.

- With almost any poem, it can be helpful to use the space around the edge of the page to jot down any ideas that occur to you. You can **use arrows or lines to show the connections** between your comment and the text. 'Tich Miller' (p. 1) is a good poem with which to try out this technique for the first time.
- A variation on this that works well with some poems is to leave enough space to **add a complete commentary** down one side of the page. With 'Miss Creedle Teaches Creative Writing' (p. 4), for example, you could write a description of what is happening in the classroom whilst Miss Creedle is talking. Or you could add the hitch-hiker's thoughts to 'The Hitch-Hiker' (p. 46).
- Do not be afraid to write on the poem itself if that allows you to understand it better. You might, for example, find it helpful to **use highlighter pens to colour code** particular parts of a poem.

  Take 'He Always . . .' (p. 24). It is not an easy poem to sort out. Try marking with one colour all the references to the things that he 'wanted to explain', and with another colour all the things that were 'square and brown inside'.
- **Diagrams** can also help you work out what is going on in a poem. You could use a spider graph, for instance, to show the connections between different ideas, or a flow diagram to illustrate a sequence of events as, for example in 'The Choosing' (p. 22).

  The advantage of diagrams is that they allow you to build up a picture as you are going along; you can stop worrying about whether you have left anything out. They also provide an opportunity for you to add your own remarks, wherever you want. 'Driving to a Death' (p. 33), for example, could be turned into a map of the journey, with your observations at the side.

Asking questions

As a rule, it is usually teachers that ask the questions, and students that provide the answers. You might be surprised by what happens when you turn the tables, and start thinking up the questions for yourself. Some questions can usefully be asked about any poem:

- What is the poem saying to you?
- How does it say it?
- Does it 'work'?

Other questions, though, only come to mind as you are working on a particular poem.

- Read 'Juan Lopez and John Ward' (p. 32), underlining the phrases in it that you find most difficult to understand. When you have finished go back to the beginning and try to write out a version of the difficult phrases that makes more sense to you.
- Take 'From the Frontier of Writing' (p. 34) or 'The Skip' (p. 27) and list the questions that you would want answered before you fully understood why the poet found himself in the situation he was in.
- Choose any poem in the collection and devise a set of questions about it for a friend to answer.

In finished form

The first section, 'Starting points', was designed to give you some ideas about how to make sense of a poem that you have just seen for the first time. It should have provided a way of sorting out anything that you found puzzling or unclear. The work in this section, 'In finished form', assumes that you have progressed beyond that point. You understand the poem, at least on the surface, but you do not yet feel confident about how best to express what you think and feel.

Before going into further detail, here is some advice that is worth following whatever kind of work you are doing on a poem.

- Read the poem silently and, if the right opportunity presents itself, read it aloud. That way you will get a sense of the rhythm and sound of the words as well as their meaning.
- Do not be timid about expressing your own feelings and opinions. The best work on poetry always manages to convey something about how the reader has responded.
- Do not feel that you have always got to have all the answers. It is in the nature of poetry that words can sometimes be doing several jobs at the same time. Be willing to make a guess, and to admit it. The word 'perhaps' can be a useful one when writing about poems.
- Do not forget to focus on the way in which poets achieve their effects. Poetry usually has designs on you; try to work out what they are.

Retelling the story

You can discover a great deal about what lies beneath the surface of a poem by turning it into a different version of itself! This is not quite such an odd idea as it sounds at first. Take the following suggestions, for instance:

- Some poems tell a story. With poems of this kind, you should be able to work out quite easily who the story teller is. Choosing a suitable poem, try retelling the story **from another point of view**.
  In 'Sons' (p. 68), for example, what do you imagine the sons are thinking when they return home late? Your version does not necessarily have to be in poetic form.
  What might the wife in 'Song of the Wagon Driver' (p. 47) write in a letter to a friend whom she has not seen for a while?

- A variation on this theme that is also worth trying requires you to retell the story **from the same point of view, but in the first person**: 'Suppose I had been him/her . . .'.
  One poem that particularly lends itself to this treatment is 'Green Beret' (p. 36). How, many years later, would the boy remember his father's death?
  'Old Father' (p. 60) also deserves a chance to tell his own story.

- There is no reason why you should not invent new characters and tell the story of what happened **from their point of view**: 'That's how I see it'.
  What might a friend, or a neighbour or the local doctor think of 'Dad' after the death of his wife in 'Long Distance II' (p. 64)?
  What would their friends and acquaintances think about the two women in 'The Choosing' (p. 22)?

Turning from the narrator to the story itself, other opportunities arise for you to re-work the original poem. Further details, for example, can be provided about the storyline, or it can be changed altogether.

- In some poems, events are referred to that we would like to know more about. There is nothing to stop you inventing **the story behind the poem**.
  In both 'About Friends' (p. 2) and 'First Ice'/'First Frost' (p. 40/41), important conversations take place around which the whole poem hinges. Try to reproduce those conversations as you think they might have happened.
  In 'Remembering St. Mary's Churchyard' (p. 18), clues are provided about 'the mad girl crying on the bench' but nothing more definite is said about her. Tell her story.

- It is always interesting to think about **what *might* have happened** in a poem instead of what did. The last verse of 'Follower' (p. 56) brings the reader back to the present. It did not have to, that was Seamus Heaney's choice. What would you have done? In another Heaney poem, 'From the Frontier of Writing' (p. 34), you might like to think about what would have happened if the soldiers had not let him through the road block.

Most of the 'follow on' work so far has concentrated on written responses to poems. It is worth remembering that there are plenty of other ways in which poetry might inspire you to be creative yourself. Here are two possibilities; you may be able to think of others for yourself.

- **Board games** offer a way of encouraging people to take decisions and think about the consequences of those decisions. That is not dramatically different from what some poems do. Think about 'The Choosing' (p. 22), for example. It could form the basis of a board game that follows the progress through life of the two women. Other poems that might be suitable include 'Christmas Thankyou's' (p. 12) and 'The Skip' (p. 27).
- If you enjoy drawing, try **drawing a poem as a cartoon**. Whether you choose to sketch a single frame, or design a cartoon strip, you will find that you are forced to select only the most important features of the poem, and that could help you to discover something about how it was written. This technique is likely to be most successful with poems like 'Three Weeks to Argentina' (p. 31) or 'Juan Lopez and John Ward' (p. 32).

The most traditional way of responding to poetry is **'the literary critical essay'**. Indeed, before GCSE, it was almost the only kind of response that was encouraged for examinations, and it continues to be an important skill that you should learn. As an indication of the kind of thing that is expected of you in an essay of this kind, look at the following instructions taken from an exam paper:

> Write about the poem, saying whether you agree with me that the words chosen by the poet, and the way he uses them, make the sensations vivid and urgent to a reader. Would you say that it is an interesting poem? Try to explain your answer – but keep to the poem as a poem.

It asks you to try and judge the *effect* of the words the poet has chosen, it asks for your *opinion* about the poem, and it reminds you that you need to *explain* what you think by drawing attention to the words on the page. Easier said than done, however.

- One way of working out the effect of the particular words chosen by the poet is to try and re-write the poem replacing all the important words with dictionary definitions of what they mean. Re-read your new version and see what has been lost. 'Rainbow' (p. 84) is one poem to which you can do dreadful damage by treating it in this way!

- As an assignment for your coursework folder, you may be expected to produce a more extended piece of writing about poetry. Included here are two 'indexes' that might give you some ideas. Using the first index, you could, for example, write about a theme and refer to the work of several different poets. Alternatively, you might choose to look at a number of poems by the same person. If this is what you would prefer to do, the second index will be more helpful.

Poems in *Wordlife* with thematic links

1 Exploring collective family memories
'About Friends' (p. 2), 'For Adam, Nearly Twelve' (p. 11), 'The Choosing' (p. 22), 'On Finding an Old Photograph' (p. 76), 'Login' (p. 54), 'Poem to My Daughter' (p. 20), 'Poem at Thirty-nine' (p. 38), 'Woodwork' (p. 45), 'If I had been called Sabrina or Ann, she said' (p. 14).

2 The power of language
'National Trust' (p. 80), 'From the Frontier of Writing' (p. 34), 'Miracle on St. David's Day' (p. 78), 'If I had been called Sabrina or Ann, she said' (p. 14).

3 Parenthood
'For Adam, Nearly Twelve' (p. 11), 'Nightride' (p. 16), 'Looking for Dad' (p. 52), 'Follower' (p. 56), 'Hit!' (p. 69), 'The Mirror' (p. 66), 'The Funeral of Father' (p. 70), 'Poem at Thirty-nine' (p. 38), 'Sons' (p. 68), 'Poem to My Daughter' (p. 20).

4 School
'Tich Miller' (p. 1), 'Miss Creedle Teaches Creative Writing' (p. 4), 'Dreaming Black Boy' (p. 8), 'He Always . . .' (p. 24), 'St. John's School' (p. 6).

5 Growing up
'The Choosing' (p. 22), 'The Skip' (p. 27), 'First Ice'/'First Frost' (p. 40/41), 'In Transit 1. The Young Soldiers' (p. 30), 'The Cleaner' (p. 42).

6 Travel/journeys
'For Adam, Nearly Twelve' (p. 11), 'Nightride' (p. 16), 'Song of the Wagon Driver' (p. 47), 'The Hitch-Hiker' (p. 46), 'Driving to a Death' (p. 33), 'From the Frontier of Writing' (p. 34), 'Bedtime Stories' (p. 62).

7 In the wild
'A Roadside Feast' (p. 65), 'Sanctuary' (p. 85), 'Finding a Sheep's Skull' (p. 55), 'The Instant' (p. 26).

8 War
'In Transit 1. The Young Soldiers' (p. 30), 'Three Weeks to Argentina' (p. 31), 'Juan Lopez and John Ward' (p. 32), 'Green Beret' (p. 36).

9 Death
'The Mirror' (p. 66), 'Driving to a Death' (p. 33), 'Quiet Eyes' (p. 58), '1113 Park Avenue' (p. 72), 'The Funeral of Father' (p. 70), 'The Flowers' (p. 73).

Poets in *Wordlife* with more than one poem included

Gillian Clarke	'Nightride' (p. 16) 'Login' (p. 54) 'Miracle on St. David's Day' (p. 78) 'My Box' (p. 86)
Wendy Cope	'Tich Miller' (p. 1) 'On Finding an Old Photograph' (p. 76)
Cynthia Fuller	'Sons' (p. 68) 'Woodwork' (p. 45)
Roger Garfitt	'In Transit 1. The Young Soldiers' (p. 30) 'The Hitch-Hiker' (p. 46)
Mick Gowar	'Christmas Thankyou's' (p. 12) 'Remembering St. Mary's Churchyard' (p. 18)
Tony Harrison	'National Trust' (p. 80) 'Long Distance II' (p. 64
Seamus Heaney	'Follower' (p. 56) 'From the Frontier of Writing' (p. 34)
Frances Horovitz	'For Adam, Nearly Twelve' (p. 11) 'Country Afternoon' (p. 74) 'Finding A Sheep's Skull' (p. 55)
Oswald Mbuyiseni Mtshali	'The Face of Hunger' (p. 7) 'Always a Suspect' (p. 81)
Anne Stevenson	Poem to My Daughter' (p. 20) 'Making Poetry' (p. 96)

Making and illustrating an anthology

The final suggestion in this section is also the most ambitious. Become your own writer, editor, illustrator, printer and publisher by producing a poetry anthology.

- *Selecting the poems*
  The first ingredient is the *poetry*. If you want to use your own, that is fine, but you do not have to do so. Like *Wordlife*, most anthologies are put together by 'editors' whose job is to collect poems that have been written by other people. They might choose poetry that they like, or poetry that is suitable for a particular

audience, such as children, or they might select a theme and link all the poems together in that way. Some possible themes are suggested in the 'index' above. Make a list of other possible themes, before selecting one for yourself.

- *Design*
  Once you have gathered together the poems that you want, you need to make some decisions about the design of the book. What size and shape do you want the pages to be? How will you bind it? How will you arrange the poems on the page? What kind of illustrations do you want? Will the book have an introduction? How long will it be?
  This is a job that can best be done in pairs. Try to team up with somebody who has got talents that complement yours. If you are good at writing, for example, work with a friend who has artistic skills.

- *Illustrations*
  The illustrations are often the key to a good anthology. However, there are no hard and fast rules to follow. Whilst you might want to illustrate the poems in a conventional way, there is no reason why you should not use photographs or 'collage'. If you decide to adopt this kind of approach, you should gather together as many old magazines as you can. They will provide a fund of illustrations, typefaces, photographs, and adverts for you to 'cannibalise' and use as part of the design for your poems. The important thing is that the final version should say something about the poem. Think of the way in which record sleeves are designed or rock videos. That might give you some ideas about how to link words and pictures.

- *Introduction*
  Finally, you need to put in the words of your own. An anthology almost always has an introduction which gives the editor a chance to say something about why they have chosen the poems and what they think of them. When you are writing your introduction, try to picture the person who might be reading it, and write directly to them. If the anthology is intended for small children, then you will not write in the same way as you might for people of your own age.

- *Readership*
  The best way, in a school, of getting a readership for your anthology is to put it in the library. You might be able to persuade your teachers that there should be a section set aside for publications by pupils. After all, the best test of whether your anthology has been successful is whether other people want to read it.

Making poetry

This final section is about writing your own poetry. Most of the suggestions are designed to help you get started, since that is often the most difficult step. After all, you can only work at a poem when you have first got something down on paper.

There are three kinds of 'starter' included here. The first category, 'Observations', is about what you might want to say. The second, 'Shapes', is about different ways in which you might say it, and the third, 'Happy accidents', is about playing around with words to see if anything happens! You may find that one of these techniques suits you better than any of the others, or that it all depends on what mood you are in. Whichever approach you adopt, do not be afraid to experiment since that is the only way in which you will surprise yourself.

Observations

- Describe something familiar from an unfamiliar point of view. One way of doing this is to put yourself in the position of somebody for whom everything is new, a child, for example, or a visitor from outer space.
- Go for a walk; write three lines about three buildings. You can adapt this technique in all sorts of ways. Try substituting 'people' for 'buildings'. It works just as successfully.
- Sometimes you can find your inspiration from books. You might try capturing your response to a book or a poem in another poem of your own. Alternatively, you might come across particular phrases or words that stick in your mind. Use them as starting points, around which you can improvise.

Shapes

- *Haiku*

  If you have never written a poem before, try starting with a **Haiku**. This is a very simple poetic form invented by the Japanese. It offers a way of freezing in time a single moment of experience:

  Ducks gliding by reeds,
  Sailing under stone bridges,
  Bobbing up and down.

  Abby Knott (aged 12)

  The rules are quite simple, and because they are so strict they can help you be economical in your choice of words so that you do not waste a syllable. The poem should be in three lines, with five syllables in the first line, seven in the second and five in the third. Haiku rarely have a 'message', and almost always leave the reader with an idea to think about in any way they wish.

- *Ballad*
  A much more complicated form is the ballad. Traditionally, a ballad tells a story, usually about some dramatic or startling events, lovers eloping, for example, or a crime of passion. In *Wordlife*, 'Song of the Wagon Driver' is a ballad. Try and imitate the rhyme and rhythm in order to create the same sense of events unfolding before our eyes.
- *Concrete or shape poems*
  Many writers have experimented with the actual shape their poems make on the page. They have tried to make the words fall into the shape of whatever it is they are writing about. Whilst none of the poems in this anthology are of this kind, you may find it a useful way of sparking off ideas for your own writing. You might like to begin by looking at 'Shapes' a small collection of shape poems in *Poetry Workshop* by Michael and Peter Benton.
- *Curses, charms and spells . . .*
  There are all kinds of writing that are almost like poetry but not quite. Examples might include riddles, curses, charms, spells, and epitaphs. Used imaginatively, you might be able to weave a poem out of any of these – a twentieth century curse, for example, or an epitaph on yourself.
- *Imitating a poetic form*
  It is possible to imitate almost any poetic form. Just identify the formulae, and make whatever changes you choose. Try 'Dear . . .' ('Christmas Thankyou's', p. 12) or 'My Dad's fatter than your Dad' ('My Dad, Your Dad', p. 44) or 'When you see . . . I tell you . . .' ('Rainbow', p. 84).

Happy accidents

- Turn to the back of any anthology of poetry, and select ten 'first lines'. Try rearranging them into a poem that makes sense!
- Make a collection of headlines from the newspaper and then create a poem by putting them together in whatever way you choose. You can do the same with public notices, graffiti or scraps of writing of almost any kind.
- List six proverbs and then chop them in half. Combine them in new ways to create new proverbs: 'Look before you spoil the broth'. Put them together to make a poem.

- Take a short poem. Change it as much as possible by altering the fewest possible words.
- In a group, try playing 'consequences' with lines of poetry, each person contributing a new line without knowing what precedes it.
- Make some large dice, and write words or phrases on each face. Then roll the dice and write a poem according to the way the dice fall out.

The activity map

The activity map, which begins overleaf, shows what happens when you start to match up the individual poems in *Wordlife* with the general approaches that have been suggested in the 'Follow on' work. All the terms used to describe possible activities are explained elsewhere, but a brief reminder may be helpful:

- *Cloze* is a way of encouraging readers to reconstruct a text from which certain words have been deleted. It will usually be introduced to a class by their teacher, but there is no reason why groups of pupils should not devise 'cloze' exercises for each other once they have become familiar with the idea.
- *Sequencing* is similar. The puzzle is provided not by deleting words, however, but by jumbling up the text so that it has to be sorted out.
- *Hot seating* is a technique most commonly used in drama. Characters (taken from the poem) are put 'on the hot seat' by being asked questions about themselves, their feelings, their opinions or their actions.

WORDLIFE: ACTIVITY MAP

Poem	Page	Suggested activities		
Tich Miller Wendy Cope	1	Group discussion focused on the last line (omitted).	Cloze: key words omitted, e.g. 'unselected'.	
About Friends Brian Jones	2	Prepared reading: how slowly can it be read?	Talk about 'Friendship' and what it means.	Selection of suitable music
Miss Creedle Teaches Creative Writing Gareth Owen	4	Parody (in a science lesson perhaps?).	Illustrations of Miss Creedle.	Tape recording?
St. John's School Fleur Adcock	6	'Memories of Primary School'	Write out the conversation with God that follows . . .	Illustrate the poem with a collage.
The Face of Hunger Oswald Mbuyiseni Mtshali	7	Link this poem with one other poem in this book and justify your choice.	What questions would you want to *ask* about the poem?	Cloze
Dreaming Black Boy James Berry	8	Delete the title. Groups provide an alternative title.		*Instant* response.

When you're a GROWN-UP Michael Rosen	10	Find photographs to match the text.	Write from your own experience.	Focus on 'baby' language.
For Adam, Nearly Twelve Frances Horovitz	11	Find out what your parents and relatives can remember about your childhood.	Link with other 'travel' poems.	Link with other poems about parenthood.
Christmas Thankyou's Mick Gowar	12	An additional verse to another relative – same rhyme scheme.	Photos/illustrations of the characters/situations.	A verse replying sarcastically to *his* sarcasm!
If I had been called Sabrina or Ann, she said Marge Piercy	14	Write a similar poem about the problems of your own name.	Compare associations that people have with particular names.	
Nightride Gillian Clarke	16	Cloze/delete last three lines?	Devise an anthology of 'Road' poems.	
Head of English Carol Ann Duffy	17	Write a letter of complaint from the poet to the Head of English after the event.	'Hot seat' the teacher.	As a group, draw up 'Rules for Writers in Schools'.

Poem	Page	Suggested activities		
Remembering St. Mary's Churchyard Mick Gowar	18	What questions need to be asked?	Focus on the girl: who? when? why?	If you did not know it was written by a man, how would you know the observers were boys?
Poem to My Daughter Anne Stevenson	20	Talk to people about how the experience of having children has changed their lives.	What might Caroline write to her mother?	In a group, discuss the meaning of the last verse.
The Choosing Liz Lochhead	22	Link with other poems.	Write from Mary's point of view.	Drama, leading to 'hot seating' of both characters.
He Always . . . Anon.	24	Small group discussion – no limits!	Who might 'anon' have been?	Link with other poems.
The Instant Denise Levertov	26	Reveal the poem bit by bit, predicting what will come next.	Share experiences of dramatic moments associated with the natural world.	
The Skip James Fenton	27	Small group discussion – no limits!	Drama: 'hot-seating' interview.	Prepared reading.

In Transit 1. The Young Soldiers Roger Garfitt	30	Delete the title.	Compare with the language and images of a recruitment advert for the armed forces.	Devise some questions of your own. (In small groups?)
Three Weeks to Argentina Gavin Ewart	31	Compile an anthology of war poems.	Link with 'Juan Lopez and John Ward'.	Compare World War I poets.
Juan Lopez and John Ward Jorge Luis Borges	32	In a small group of two or three, discuss the poem and agree a fitting epitaph to be carved on each man's gravestone.	Link with 'Three Weeks to Argentina' and 'A Game of Soldiers' by Jan Needle.	Write letters home.
Driving to a Death William Scammell	33	Cloze, with 'mood' words deleted.	Link with poems on a similar theme.	
From the Frontier of Writing Seamus Heaney	34	Discuss the *two* journeys. Report back.	Delete the title.	What questions need to be asked?
Green Beret Ho Thien	36	Analyse the poet's viewpoint and the language that he uses to put it across.	Write from Green Beret's point of view.	Read aloud!

Poem	Page	Suggested activities		
Poem at Thirty-nine Alice Walker	38	Write 'Poem at Nineteen'. What might Alice Walker at a younger age have thought of her father?	Delete the last two lines. What kind of person has she become as a result of him?	Use the formula: 'How I miss . . .' for your own poetry.
First Ice/First Frost Andre Voznesensky	40/41	See page 100.		
The Cleaner U.A. Fanthorpe	42	'Hot seat' the cleaner.	Write from a male cleaner's point of view!	
My Dad, Your Dad Kit Wright	44	Write a poem for younger children.		
Woodwork Cynthia Fuller	45	What might the father have thought had he sat and watched his daughter without her being aware of it?	Compare with 'Poem at Thirty-nine'.	
The Hitch-Hiker Roger Garfitt	46	Answer the question!	Illustrate it.	With this poem, and the three preceding it, compare *how* the poets have achieved the mood of each.

Song of the Wagon Driver B.S. Johnson	47	Additional verses incorporating the incident in 'For Adam, Nearly Twelve'.	'Song of the . . .' (different occupation; same format).	Photographs to illustrate.
The Rovers Kit Wright	48	Write an objective match report and compare with Father's own version.		Prepared reading: what accent would you use?
Looking for Dad Brian Patten	52	Compile an anthology of 'Family' poems, or of poems that merge humour and pathos.		A verse written on the 29th *July*.
Login Gillian Clarke	54	Photographs again	An account from another point of view.	Small group discussion: own agenda.
Finding a Sheep's Skull Frances Horovitz	55	Cloze	Small group discussion: own agenda.	
Follower Seamus Heaney	56	Cloze	Compare with other poems about fathers (e.g. 'Woodwork').	
Quiet Eyes John Latham	58	Delete title: small group discussion.	Link with poems on a similar theme.	Open-ended group discussion.

Poem	Page	Suggested activities		
Old Father Hugh Boatswain	60	Drama: 'hot seat'.	Open-ended small group discussion.	Exploration of dialect.
Bedtime Stories Jenny Moy	62	Delete the title and all references to journeying and reading: discuss in small groups.	Write about your own early memories of learning to read; get your parents to do the same.	'TRAY' of part of the poem, or, if you are lucky enough to use that version of the program which allows you to 'turn over', the whole poem.
Long Distance II Tony Harrison	64	Immediate written response.	Another title?	Delete last words: small group discussion.
A Roadside Feast Peter Redgrove	65	Reveal the poem line by line, inviting predictions.	Agree on one more line.	Cloze: delete the verbs.
The Mirror Paul Muldoon	66	Write a five line epitaph, *using* the poem.		
Sons Cynthia Fuller	68	Write from the point of view of the sons.	'Hot seat' one of the sons after he has returned home later than was agreed.	Discussion about the relationship between parents and their children. What is the *ideal*?

Hit! Pete Morgan	69	'TRAY'	Jumble the verses up. Can they be unscrambled?	
The Funeral of Father Denise King	70	Write from another point of view.		
1113 Park Avenue Alice Kavounas	72	'TRAY'		
The Flowers Selima Hill	73	Link with 'Quiet Eyes'.	Delete the daughter's words (last verse) and, in pairs, suggest what she might have said.	
Country Afternoon Frances Horovitz	74	Delete the title.	Who are 'we'? (In small groups?)	Answer the last question in the poem.
On Finding an Old Photograph Wendy Cope	76	Find some appropriate photos; then explore the family memories that go with them.		Delete last line and discuss. Write his epitaph.
Miracle on St. David's Day Gillian Clarke	78	A nurse's report of what happened for the hospital files.	How does the poem *work*?	Read it aloud!

Poem	Page	Suggested activities		
National Trust Tony Harrison	80	Delete title: speculate about an alternative.	Delete last line; what might the Cornish mean?	Open-ended small group discussion.
Always a Suspect Oswald Mbuyiseni Mtshali	81		Cloze	Leave out the dialogue. What was said? (In small groups)
The Fat Black Woman Goes Shopping Grace Nichols	82	In small groups delete all references to sex and race. What difference does it make?	Compare 'Old Father'.	
Rainbow John Agard	84	Present it musically.	And visually.	Delete final six lines or the first word of the last line. What difference does it make?
Sanctuary Duncan Forbes	85	'TRAY'	Delete title.	Sequencing.
My Box Gillian Clarke	86	Delete the title: find another!	What questions should be asked?	

Poetry resources

Books

R. Andrews, *Into Poetry* (Ward Lock Education, 1983).
M. Benton and P. Benton, *Examining Poetry: a Practical Guide for 15–18 year olds* (Hodder & Stoughton, 1986); *Poetry Workshop* (The English Universities Press, 1975)
M. Benton and G. Fox, *Teaching Literature 9–14* (Oxford, 1985)
P. Benton, *Pupil, Teacher, Poem* (Hodder & Stoughton, 1986)
S. Brownjohn, *Does it Have to Rhyme?* (Hodder & Stoughton, 1980); *What Rhymes with Secret?* (Hodder & Stoughton, 1982)
P. Corbett and B. Moses, *Catapults and Kingfishers* (Oxford, 1986)
J. Dixon, L. Stratta et al, *Examining Poetry: the Need for Change* (SREB, 1986)
J. Foggin, *Write to the Point: Making a Poetry Anthology* (Glasgow, 1986)
HMI Publication, *Teaching Poetry in the Secondary School: an HMI View* (DES, 1987)
T. Hughes, *Poetry in the Making* (Faber, 1967)
E. Lunzer and K. Gardner, *The Effective Use of Reading* (Heinemann, 1979); *Learning From the Written Word* (Oliver & Boyd, 1984)
ed. J. Medlin, *Poetry Live: British and Irish Poetry 1987* (Book Trust and The Poetry Society, 1987)
NATE Publication, *NATEPACK ONE: POETRY* (NATE)
ed. P. Smyth, *Talking and Learning in Small Groups: pupils aged 12–13 in conversation about a poem* (SLDC/Longman, 1985)
S. Tunnicliffe, *Poetry Experience* (Methuen, 1985)

Societies and organisations

The Poetry Society, 21 Earls Court Square, London SW5 9DE
The Arvon Foundation (poetry writing courses) at Lumb Bank, Hebden Bridge, West Yorkshire HX7 6DF *and* Totleigh Barton, Sheepwash, near Beauworthy, Devon EX21 5NS
Writers in schools: contact your regional Arts Association

The author and publishers are grateful to the following for permission to reproduce copyright material:

Photographs
Ed Barber (p. 9); BBC Hulton Picture Library (pp. 15, 43, 57, 77); Mark Edwards Picture Library for Publishers (p. 71); Sally and Richard Greenhill (pp. 3, 21, 57, 83); Anthony Hayes (p. 29); Judah Passow/Network (p. 35); Sporting Pictures (UK) Ltd (p. 51).

Poems
A. D. Peters & Co Ltd Writers' Agents, for 'The Skip' by James Fenton, published by The Salamander Press and King Penguin; Anvil Press Poetry Ltd for 'Head of English' by Carol Ann Duffy from *Standing Female Nude*; Bloodaxe Books, The Enitharmon Press and Roger Garfitt for 'For Adam, Nearly Twelve' by Frances Horovitz from *Collected Poems*, published by Bloodaxe Books in association with The Enitharmon Press; The Bodley Head Ltd for 'About Friends' by Brian Jones from *Spitfire on the Northern Line*; Carcanet Press Ltd for 'In Transit, 1. The Young Soldiers' and 'The Hitch-Hiker' by Roger Garfitt, and for 'Login', 'Miracle on St. David's Day', 'My Box' and 'Nightride' by Gillian Clarke from *Selected Poems*; Century Hutchinson Publishing Group Ltd for 'Three Weeks to Argentina' by Gavin Ewart from *The Young Pobble's Guide to his Toes*; Chatto & Windus and The Hogarth Press for 'The Flowers' by Selima Hill from *Saying Hello at the Station*; Collins Publishers for 'Christmas Thankyou's' and 'Remembering St Mary's Churchyard' by Mick Gowar from *Swings and Roundabouts*, and for 'Miss Creadle Teaches Creative Writing' by Gareth Owen from *Song of the City*; David Higham Associates Ltd for 'Poem at Thirty-nine' by Alice Walker from *Horses Make a Landscape Look More Beautiful*, published by The Women's Press; Faber and Faber Ltd for 'From the Frontier of Writing' and 'Follower' by Seamus Heaney from *The Haw Lantern* and *Death of a Naturalist*, respectively, also for 'The Mirror' by Paul Muldoon from *Quoof* and for 'Tich Miller' and 'On Finding an Old Photograph' by Wendy Cope, from *Making Cocoa for Kingsley Amis*; Fraser & Dunlop Scripts Ltd for 'Long Distance II' and 'National Trust' by Tony Harrison; John Latham for his poem 'Quiet Eyes'; Littlewood Press for 'Sons' and 'Woodwork' by Cynthia Fuller; Martin Secker & Warburg Ltd for 'Sanctuary' by Duncan Forbes from *August Autumn* and for 'Hit' by Pete Morgan, from *A Winter Visitor*; MBA Literary Agents Ltd and the Estate of B. S. Johnson 1988 for 'Song of the Wagon Driver' by B. S. Johnson, first published by Constable and Co Ltd, 1964; Oxford University Press for 'Making Poetry', and 'Poem to My Daughter' by Anne Stevenson from *Selected Poems 1956–1986* and *Minute by Glass Minute*, respectively, and for 'St John's School' by Fleur Adcock, from *Selected Poems*; Penguin Books Ltd for 'The Rovers' by Kit Wright from *Hot Dog and Other Poems*, published by Kestrel Books; Peterloo Poets for 'Driving to a Death' by William Scammell from *Jouissance* and for 'The Cleaner' by U. A. Fanthorpe from *Voices Off*; Polygon for 'The Choosing' by Liz Lockhead from *Dreaming Frankenstein and Collected Poems*; Serpent's Tail for 'Rainbow' by John Agard; Virago Press Ltd for 'The Fat Black Woman Goes Shopping' by Grace Nichols from *The Fat Black Woman's Poems.*

Every effort has been made to contact the holders of copyright material but if any have been inadvertently overlooked the publishers will be pleased to make the necessary arrangements at the first opportunity.